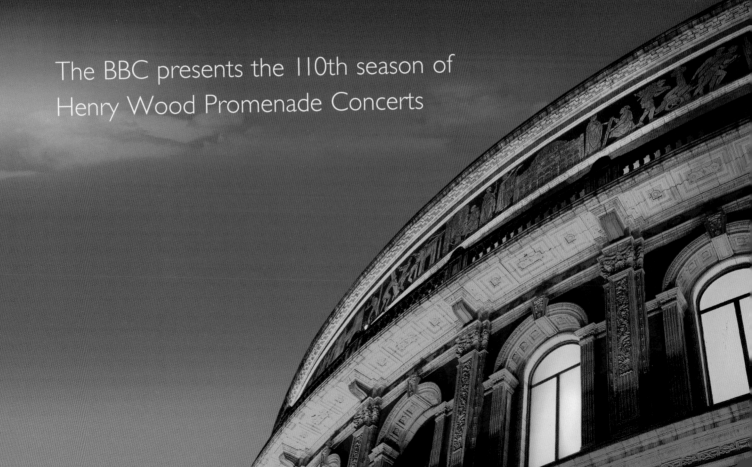

PROMS

16 JULY – 11 SEPTEMBER 2004

The BBC presents the 110th season of
Henry Wood Promenade Concerts

The Proms: 1895–2004

The Proms were founded to bring the best of classical music to a wide audience in an informal setting. From the outset, part of the audience has always stood in the 'promenade'. Prom places originally cost just a shilling; today, standing places at the Royal Albert Hall still cost only £4.00, and over 1,000 tickets go on sale for every concert from an hour beforehand. Programmes have always mixed the great classics with what Henry Wood, first conductor of the Proms, called his 'novelties' – rare works and premieres. **1895** The 26-year-old Wood is chosen to launch the Promenade Concerts at the newly opened Queen's Hall; Wood conducts the Proms throughout their first 50 years. **1927** The BBC takes over the running of the Proms. **1930** The new BBC Symphony Orchestra becomes the orchestra of the Proms; the BBC's own orchestras still provide the backbone of the season. **1941** The Proms move to the Royal Albert Hall after the Queen's Hall is gutted in an air raid. **1942** The BBC SO shares the season for the first time with another orchestra: the LPO. **1944** Henry Wood dies shortly after celebrating his Proms jubilee. **1947** First televised Last Night. **1953** First out-of-London orchestra at the Proms: the Hallé, from Manchester, under John Barbirolli. **1960** First BBC Proms commission: William Alwyn's *Derby Day*. **1961** First complete opera at the Proms: Mozart's *Don Giovanni*, brought by Glyndebourne Festival. **1966** First foreign orchestra at the Proms: the Moscow Radio Orchestra, under Gennady Rozhdestvensky. **1968** First Friday-night First Night. **1970** First Late Night Prom: cult pop group The Soft Machine. **1971** First 'world music' Prom: sitar-player Imrat Khan. **1974** First Pre-Prom Talks. **1994** The Proms celebrate their 100th season with a retrospective of past premieres. **1995** The Proms celebrate their centenary year with a season of new commissions. **1996** First Prom in the Park; first Proms Chamber Music series. **1997** First Proms solo recital. **1998** First Blue Peter Family Prom. **2001** First 'Nation's Favourite' Prom. **2002** The Proms go digital on BBC4. **2003** The Proms go interactive on digital TV and the internet. **2004** More Proms on TV than ever before.

The BBC: bringing the Proms to you, wherever you are – on radio, television and the internet www.bbc.co.uk/proms

BBC

Welcome to the BBC Proms 2004!

The BBC Proms: making inspirational music available to all

We welcome the world's great conductors, including Pierre Boulez, Sir Colin Davis, Valery Gergiev, Christoph Eschenbach, Bernard Haitink, Mariss Jansons, Sir Charles Mackerras, André Previn and Sir Simon Rattle, as well as the outstanding conductors of the leading British and BBC orchestras. Alongside the great classics of orchestral music, they explore new areas of the repertory, rarities and premieres.

EAST/WEST: Cellist Yo-Yo Ma and his acclaimed Silk Road Ensemble take the Proms on a journey through diverse musical idioms and instruments; Chinese-American composers Tan Dun, Bright Sheng and Zhou Long offer the adventurous sonorities of their new music, alongside the many Western composers inspired by the music of the East, from Mahler to Britten.

Back to Bohemia: An anniversary-led survey of Czech music, from the splendour of Janáček's *Glagolitic Mass* and Dvořák's rarely heard opera *Dimitrij* to music by earlier Bohemian masters Biber, Zelenka and Mysliveček.

England at the Crossroads: The year when Elgar, Holst and Delius all died also brought the promise of a new renaissance, with the births of Sir Harrison Birtwistle, whose latest Proms commission sets the poetry of Alfred Brendel, and of Sir Peter Maxwell Davies, whose appointment as Master of the Queen's Music we celebrate.

And more: We launch a four-year Proms *Ring* cycle. A wealth of early music sits alongside new works from the world's finest composers, from John Adams to Kaija Saariaho. Leonard Slatkin celebrates his 60th birthday in his farewell season with the BBC Symphony Orchestra. The Royal Albert Hall's historic organ is back.

This year BBC FOUR will televise three weeks of the season, bringing more Proms to television than ever before. As always, every concert is live on BBC Radio 3. And on the Last Night, BBC Proms in the Park once again takes place in all four nations of the UK. Increased digital and online interactivity, further books of Proms programme notes and new CD recordings of last year's concerts all add to the ever-expanding reach of the Proms. Enjoy the season!

Nicholas Kenyon

Nicholas Kenyon
Director, BBC Proms

EAST/WEST

A two-way traffic

**'East is East, and West is West, and never the twain shall meet'?
Neil Sorrell examines the many ways the West has absorbed
the music of the East, and vice versa, from Marco Polo to today**

Western traders had been bringing back riches from the East long before composers thought of exploring its music. In the Middle Ages, Marco Polo visited China, Arab civilisation made a huge impact in Moorish Spain and Eastern instruments like the oboe and lute were brought back to Europe from the Crusades. So already at that time the music and culture of the Occident had absorbed some oriental influences. The search for spices and non-European raw materials was a prime motivation for voyages to distant and exotic lands. Ultimately, this led to colonisation. When the reverse happened and an oriental power, the Ottoman Empire, threatened Western Europe – roughly from the 15th to the 19th centuries – the music the invading armies brought with them gained a firm foothold.

Mozart and Beethoven both wrote so-called 'Turkish music', but they were by no means the first composers to succumb to the fad (as it certainly was). More than a century earlier, Louis XIV's court composer, Jean-Baptiste Lully, had composed a 'Turkish ceremony' for Molière's 'comédie-ballet' *Le bourgeois*

gentilhomme and had himself played the part of the Grand Mufti in its 1670 premiere. His attitude epitomised these early responses. Authenticity is a minor concern, compared to parody, satire and downright ridicule. Thus Lully's Mufti speaks in a ludicrous 'lingua franca',

or pidgin French, largely composed of nonsense syllables. European art – and, by association, European power – had to appear superior to Turkish.

Such disrespect was all very well in France. Further East, people had every reason to live in fear of the Ottoman Empire. Vienna was, for a long time, on the front line and twice narrowly escaped sacking, first in 1529 and again in 1683. Understandably, it was with more fear than fascination that people there first heard the sound of the Janissary bands. No sooner had the threat receded, though, than composers began to affect the *alla turca* style, with its characteristic use of percussion – cymbals, triangle, Turkish crescent (or 'jingling Johnny') and big bass drum. These instruments were in turn soon absorbed into many of Europe's own military bands, alongside the more traditional wind and brass. This mingling of the two types of marching band explains why the famous episode in the finale of Beethoven's 'Choral' Symphony can be heard both as 'Turkish music' and as a typical German village band.

During the 19th century all kinds of orientalisms abounded, especially in

opera, but in general the emphasis was on exotic colour rather than real engagement. So when Debussy was bowled over by the 'infinite arabesque' of the Javanese gamelan music he heard at the 1889 Universal Exposition in Paris – declaring that its polyphony made Palestrina's seem like child's play – a new age dawned. From this point, roughly coinciding with the start of the 20th century, we can observe a process, from the partially informed enthusiasm of Debussy towards a total immersion in other cultures, and what the American ethnomusicologist Mantle Hood termed 'bi-musicality'. Debussy's encounter with Eastern culture helped clarify his thinking about the future direction of Western music and freed him, to some extent, from Wagner's oppressive influence. He certainly used pentatonic scales in 'Pagodes', the first of his three *Estampes*

of 1903 (and some say the pentatonic opening of *La mer* is meant to suggest the sun rising in the East!), but how far his enthusiasm for Javanese gamelan was transformed into detailed knowledge, and whether he ever intended any direct imitation of it, remain debatable.

Ravel's interest in orientalism was more persistent, if not more profound.

It can be heard at its most blatant in the 'Little Ugly, Empress of the Pagodas' episode in his fairy-tale suite *Mother Goose* (1910), and rather more subtly in the chiming pentatonicism and gong-like punctuation of 'La vallée des cloches' (the last of his five *Miroirs* of 1905) – whose gamelan-derived sounds are made yet more explicit in Percy Grainger's orchestration – and in the yearning sensuality of his earlier oriental song-cycle *Shéhérazade* (1903).

The name of the story-telling heroine of the *1,001 Nights* conjures up Rimsky-Korsakov's famous orchestral masterpiece. Russia, both in Western European consciousness and in the minds of many Russian composers, is already halfway to the Orient, although Arabia is much more part of the exotic 'other' than, say, Kyrgyzstan, which was still part of the USSR when Shostakovich wrote his *Overture on Russian and Kirghiz Folk Themes* after a short visit there in 1963.

Debussy's great contemporary, Gustav Mahler, made one excursion into oriental – specifically Chinese – culture, producing probably his finest work: the song-symphony *Das Lied von der Erde*.

A generation later, Olivier Messiaen experienced a defining encounter with Indian music, not in performance, or in person – since he always preferred not to visit India itself, lest his image of the country and its culture be shattered – but in the pages of an encyclopedia. Which is where, in the early 1930s, he found an entry on the so-called *deçi-tâlas* – obsolete rhythmic devices derived from a medieval Sanskrit treatise – that were soon to become so integrated into his unmistakable style as to become a distinguishing feature

ABOVE
Programme for the Javanese display at the 1889 Universal Exhibition in Paris

LEFT
Shiva Nataraja: the Hindu god of dance and destruction

BELOW
The Pagoda in Kew Gardens: at the time of its completion in 1762, it was the most accurate reconstruction of a Chinese building in Europe

PROM 58

Claude Debussy (1862–1918)
Khamma (orch. Charles Koechlin)

Khamma is one of those strange works, inhabiting an exotic, sensual other-world, that occupied Debussy in the last years of his life. It was commissioned in 1911 by the Canadian dancer Maude Allan for a ballet in which an ancient Egyptian dancing-girl sacrifices herself to the sun-god Amon-Ra in order to save her city. Debussy affected to despise what he called 'this wretched little Anglo-Egyptian ballet'. Angered by Allan's interference, he left the orchestration of all but the first few bars to his brilliant younger colleague, Charles Koechlin (1867–1950) and, in the event, the work was not finally performed until 1947, almost 30 years after Debussy's death. But the music he wrote is, needless to say, neither English nor Egyptian (he himself claimed it represented 'the most recent discoveries in harmonic chemistry') and deserves to be rescued from the near-total obscurity in which it has languished since its completion in 1912.

LEFT The Great Temple of Amon-Ra at Karnak: by Jean-Charles Langlois (1789–1870)

British Library (above); courtesy of the UCLA Ethnomusicology Archive (below and inset)

PROM 57

Gustav Mahler (1860–1911)
Das Lied von der Erde

In composing *Das Lied von der Erde* (The Song of the Earth) in the summer of 1908, Mahler responded to the terrible events of the preceding year – the death of his elder daughter Maria and the diagnosis of his own (ultimately fatal) heart condition – with his most personal, deeply felt and radiantly life-affirming score. It's an orchestral cycle of six eighth-century Chinese poems that Mahler had found, in German translation, in Hans Bethge's 1907 anthology, *Die chinesische Flöte* (The Chinese Flute). How far the music follows Chinese models is hard to say. Mahler had, it seems, heard recordings of Chinese music. Certainly, the pentatonic scale – that most familiar form of musical 'chinoiserie' – pervades the entire score; but it also makes much use of heterophony, a kind of counterpoint, found especially in Far Eastern music, based on simultaneous variations of the same melody. The sense of loneliness, isolation and emptiness – especially in the final song, 'Der Abschied' (The Farewell) – is largely achieved through sparse, even fragile textures, gong sounds and the use of drones. The resulting sound-world is so unusual that Mahler must surely have had some genuine Chinese music in mind when he wrote it.
See also pages 142–3

ABOVE
Figurine of a Chinese dancing girl

BELOW
Balinese gamelan players: one of the many hundreds of photographs taken by Colin McPhee in the 1930s

PROM 49

Colin McPhee (1900–64)
Tabuh-tabuhan

There are many reasons why the Indonesian gamelan (percussion orchestra) has exerted such a special influence over Western musicians, not least the visual and aural beauty of its hand-crafted instruments. A complete gamelan set, including instruments in both *sléndro* and *pélog* – the two tuning systems unique to the Indonesian archipelago – probably constitutes the world's largest concert ensemble after the Western symphony orchestra. But, unlike the latter, a gamelan is a set of instruments that stays together and only really functions as an ensemble, rather than an assembly of solo instruments belonging to individual players.

Although the British lagged behind the Dutch, Americans and Australians in the systematic study of gamelan music, they were among the first Europeans to respond to it. Stamford Raffles, the British Governor of Java, brought back two gamelan sets upon his return to Britain in 1816, and it was at the Crystal Palace, in 1851, that gamelans were first heard at any of the 19th century's great universal exhibitions.

In America, it was the composer Colin McPhee *(inset, above right)* who was primarily responsible for creating an interest in gamelan. He spent several years living in Bali in the 1930s and, as well as transcribing the music and using it in his own compositions – of which the 1936 Pulitzer Prize-winning toccata *Tabuh-tabuhan* is the best known – wrote one of the most authoritative studies of it. Largely thanks to him, the gamelan became the backbone of practical work in American university music departments in the 1950s and 1960s. As a result, Americans took it to their hearts, not only playing it but composing for it (rather than just imitating its sounds on Western instruments), and even building their own versions, which in turn became the focus of yet more playing and composing.

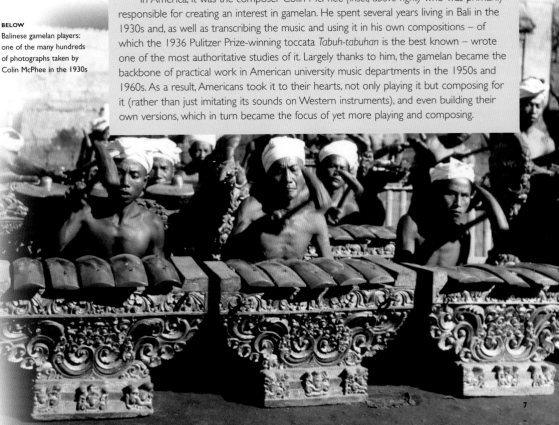

Benjamin Britten (1913–76)
Curlew River

While Britten regularly used gamelan-like sounds, usually to evoke a sense of other-worldly exoticism, even in such non-Eastern contexts as *Paul Bunyan*, *Peter Grimes*, *The Turn of the Screw* and *Owen Wingrave*, it is only in his exotic 1957 ballet *The Prince of the Pagodas* (Prom 62) that he actually imitates and quotes the Balinese gamelan music he had heard first-hand during his tour of Asia in 1955–6 and had earlier played in two-piano arrangements with Colin McPhee in New York in the early 1940s. Britten's attitude to Japanese culture was rather more antipathetic at first, but when he attended a Noh play during his visit to Tokyo in 1956, the experience was powerful and produced a stroke of genius. Rather than imitate Japanese music directly or quote from it (as Puccini had done in *Madam Butterfly* or indeed as Sullivan had done, almost 20 years earlier, in *The Mikado*), Britten transposed the action of the Japanese play *Sumidagawa* (Sumida River) to the fens of East Anglia and renamed it *Curlew River*. The story of a mad woman (sung by a tenor – Britten's partner, Peter Pears, in the first performances) frantically searching for her lost (in fact, dead) son remains the same. But in transplanting the austere, ritualistic world and Buddhist ethos of the original Noh play to a medieval monastic setting, and framing the action with plainsong, Britten created a new form of opera, which he called the 'church parable'.

of it. Messiaen's modal melodic language also has affinities with Indian *râgas*, though it does not directly use them. His encounter with Balinese gamelan music at the Paris exhibition of 1931, and on 78rpm records heard at the Musée Guimet, followed the more familiar pattern. In his *Turangalîla Symphony*, for example, he gave prominence to an expanded percussion section – and actually called the bewitching tuned section a 'gamelang' – but did not use real gamelan music or try to imitate it literally. The work's title is made up of two Sanskrit words which, for Messiaen, signified the divine interplay of life and death, time and rhythm. The combination of Indian and Indonesian influences is significant, but the work is really about love and joy: it is perhaps the greatest ode to joy since Beethoven and the greatest interpretation of the Tristan and Isolde myth since Wagner.

Another Frenchman who visited the 1931 exhibition was Francis Poulenc. He responded to the Balinese music he heard there by producing, just a year later, what

is perhaps the earliest pastiche of it, his Concerto for Two Pianos. This uses the standard orchestra but imitates (mainly in the two solo parts) the shimmering polyphony of the Balinese gamelan.

In 1935 Poulenc came to London to perform his new double concerto with his friend Benjamin Britten. Britten's involvement with Eastern music is quite complicated and especially fascinating. Having first been introduced to Balinese music by the American composer and musicologist Colin McPhee in the early 1940s, Britten visited the island himself in 1956, when he not only spent time listening to gamelan groups but actually jotted down bits of their music. When he then incorporated some of this material, along with music transcribed by McPhee, in his 1957 ballet *The Prince of the Pagodas* (based, like Ravel's 'Little Ugly', on the 17th-century fairy-tale *Serpentin vert* by Mme D'Aulnoy), he managed to find matching colours within the Western symphony orchestra so skilfully that one is almost fooled into thinking one is listening to a genuine gamelan.

Britten's tour to the East also took in a visit to Japan, the fruits of which are most obvious in his Noh-based 'church parable', *Curlew River*, written in 1964.

If Britten was smitten by his visit to Bali, Constant Lambert's 1929 set of *Eight Poems of Li-Po* were inspired by a very different passion, his unrequited love for the Chinese-American film star Anna May Wong.

The English generation before Britten and Lambert had produced at least one figure who demonstrated a deep interest in the Orient. Gustav Holst used a Japanese

TOP LEFT
Peter Pears as the Madwoman in the 1964 premiere of *Curlew River* in Orford Church

BOTTOM LEFT
Benjamin Britten *(far right)* and Pears *(far left)* with the Prince and Princess of Hesse, photographed in Balinese dress on 20 January 1956

TOP
The man with the 'little list': George Grossmith as Ko-Ko in the 1885 premiere of Gilbert and Sullivan's *The Mikado* at the Savoy Theatre

ABOVE
Rosina Storchio as Cio-Cio-San in the 1904 premiere of Puccini's *Madam Butterfly* at La Scala, Milan

Gustav Holst (1874–1934)
Sāvitri

RIGHT
The legend of Sāvitri: an 11th-century sandstone carving from southern Rajasthan or Madhya Pradesh

BELOW
The Red Detachment of Women: John Adams's pastiche of a real Cultural Revolutionary ballet, from the ENO revival of his 1987 opera *Nixon in China*

BOTTOM
John Cage, out shopping for microbiotic food in Ferrara, Italy, in 1991

For his chamber opera *Sāvitri* (1908), Holst wrote his own libretto – in an archaic, slightly biblical English – based on an episode from the Hindu epic, the *Mahābhārata*. The subject is simple – how the loving wife Sāvitri saves the life of her husband Satyavan by outwitting Death, who, in the work's dramatically unaccompanied opening, announces that he has come to claim him. The use of just three characters, plus a wordless female chorus, an ensemble of only 12 musicians and the simplest action within a single 30-minute span, all make *Sāvitri* one of the easiest and most effective operas to stage.

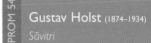

lullaby in his *Japanese Suite* (1915) and, in one of his boldest strokes, based the last movement of his 'oriental suite' *Beni Mora* (1910) on the hypnotic repetition of a tune he had heard on a cycling holiday in Algeria. But as far as his interest in non-European cultures went, the pervasive force was India. 'Culture' is here the operative word, since Holst's daughter Imogen claimed that – though he taught himself Sanskrit, set a number of Hindu texts (notably his beautiful settings of *Choral Hymns from the Rig Veda*) and composed two operas on Hindu subjects (*Sita* and *Sāvitri*) – he nevertheless knew nothing at all about Indian music.

The composer as fieldworker adds an important dimension to the process under discussion. Britten, Holst and others undertook fieldwork, while Debussy, Mahler and Messiaen (despite his global trips) did not. Doubling as an ethnomusicologist does not bestow

greatness on a composer – though the name Bartók rings through the decades as the supreme example of someone who achieved greatness in both spheres – but it does mark a sea-change in the response of Western composers to other cultures.

It is no coincidence that this seems to have happened most in America, where ethnomusicology expanded to embrace 'bi-musicality' (through performance) and where composers, especially on the West Coast, have long been conscious of an Asian heritage as strong as the assumed European one. John Cage's interest in Indian aesthetics was first manifested in his 1947 ballet *The Seasons*, while his later use of 'chance operations' was initially inspired by the gift of a copy of the Chinese oracle guide, the *I Ching*.

Cage's friend and occasional collaborator, Lou Harrison (1917–2003), is one of two Eastern-oriented American composers – the other being Terry Riley,

creator of the early minimalist classic *In C* – whom John Adams names as the 'guardian deities' of his new Jack Kerouac-inspired concerto, *The Dharma at Big Sur* (UK premiere, Prom 49), in which, Adams has said, the solo writing for amplified violin was heavily influenced by Eastern playing styles, from India, Iran and Afghanistan. Adams, of course, cheekily composed his own pastiche version of Madame Mao's favourite ballet, *The Red Detachment of Women*, for his 1987 opera *Nixon in China*.

It is no coincidence that America has attracted so many composers from the Far East to study and even settle there. While perhaps the most famous Asian classical composer of recent times, Tōru Takemitsu (1930–96), preferred to stay in his native Japan – though composing in what is often a strongly Western-style idiom – a new generation of Chinese composers has come West.

Zhou Long (b. 1953), Bright Sheng (b. 1955) and Tan Dun (b. 1957) all have much in common besides their place and time of birth. All three lived through the Cultural Revolution. While Zhou Long and Tan Dun (whose 1998 *Water Concerto* was written in memory of Takemitsu) were sent to work in the fields – not quite the same thing as fieldwork in the Western sense but with somewhat similar ethnomusicological results, in terms of their absorption of rural folk traditions and rituals, and, in Tan's case, Peking Opera style – Bright Sheng managed to continue working as a musician but still undertook a deep study of folk music, which has remained an important influence on his style. All three later went on to further musical studies in America, where they soon made their homes and, increasingly, their reputations.

Tan Dun's recent work in film – his Oscar-winning score for Ang Lee's *Crouching Tiger, Hidden Dragon* – has brought this new synthesis of East/West styles to a vast new audience.

ABOVE
Hear no evil: a Peking Opera player as the Monkey King

LEFT
Tan Dun, who will conduct his own *Out of Peking Opera* and *Water Concerto*

PROM 6
Zhou Long (b. 1953)
The Immortal • BBC World Service commission: world premiere

Born in Beijing in 1953, Zhou Long *(inset)* was sent to work on a farm during the Cultural Revolution but enrolled at the Central Conservatory of Music as soon as it reopened in 1977. After two years as composer-in-residence for China's National Broadcasting Orchestra, he went to America for further study in 1985, becoming a US citizen in 1999. A finalist in the first Masterprize competition, he is married to the composer Chen Yi, whose Percussion Concerto was played at last year's Proms. *The Immortal* is, he says, 'a tribute to the Chinese artists and intellectuals of the 20th century. Having grown up during the Cultural Revolution, I know from personal experience the struggles and hardships that past generations have endured to remain true to these eternal ideals. These memories remain with me to this day – and through the abstract language of music I am recognising and portraying their enduring spirit.'

EAST/WEST works at the Proms

Adams	The Dharma at Big Sur	Prom 49
Bartók	The Miraculous Mandarin – Suite	Prom 28
Beethoven	Symphony No. 9, 'Choral'	Prom 67
Bright Sheng	The Song and Dance of Tears	Prom 38
Britten	Curlew River	Prom 17
	The Prince of the Pagodas (excerpt)	Prom 62
Cage	The Seasons	Prom 24
Debussy	Estampes	PCM 4
	Khamma (orch. Koechlin)	Prom 58
Holst	Choral Hymns from the Rig Veda – Group 3 (selection)	Prom 48
	Sāvitri	Prom 54
Lambert	Eight Poems of Li-Po	Prom 54
McPhee	Tabuh-tabuhan	Prom 49
Mahler	Das Lied von der Erde	Prom 57
Messiaen	Turangalîla Symphony	Prom 38
Puccini	Madam Butterfly – Humming Chorus	Prom 74
Ravel	Miroirs – La vallée des cloches (orch. Grainger)	Prom 49
	Shéhérazade – trois poèmes	Prom 29
	Shéhérazade – ouverture de féerie	Prom 33
Shostakovich	Overture on Russian and Kirghiz Folk Themes	Prom 24
Sullivan	The Mikado – 'I've got a little list'	Prom 74
Takemitsu	Twill by Twilight	Prom 29
Tan Dun	Out of Peking Opera; Water Concerto	Prom 24
Zhou Long	The Immortal	Prom 6

The internet of antiquity

In 1998 the Chinese-American cellist Yo-Yo Ma set up the Silk Road Project to explore cultural exchanges along the old trade routes from China. As Ma and his Ensemble prepare to make their Proms debut in a series of three concerts, Michael Church recalls how he saw them in action, out in the 'Stans', last spring

As its name implies, the old Silk Road – which connected the Mediterranean to China – was primarily a conduit for commodities, but art and science travelled along it too: the secrets of ceramics and lacquer, plus gunpowder, mathematics and the printing press – and, above all, musical styles and instruments. In Chinese-American cellist Yo-Yo Ma's neat phrase, this was 'the internet of antiquity'.

Twenty-five years of globetrotting have taught Ma to look out for unexpected connections – 'like the medieval plectrum decorated with an elephant, a Persian man and a Chinese landscape. Or the correspondence between the Japanese *biwa* and the Middle Eastern *oud*.' The research he did on the cello's precursors propelled him towards the Persian

kemancheh (spike-fiddle), and thence to the Tuvan horse-head fiddle, and the Chinese *erhu*. 'World after world opened up, and became possible to explore.'

Those ancient Persian and Chinese instruments may not yet lie comfortably under Ma's fingers, but last spring I watched him extemporise brilliantly on the Tuvan fiddle in three Central Asian capitals. How he got there, and what his purpose was, makes a story with deep resonance for our times.

His initial decision was to launch a contemporary Silk Road, whose trade would be in music. With backing from the Ford Foundation, and local support from the Aga Khan Trust for Culture, Ma created a project whereby Asian musicians – plus hand-picked young virtuosos from America – would come together to create new works, play them at points along the old route, and hold workshops for local

RIGHT
Yo-Yo Ma swaps his cello for a Tuvan horse-head fiddle

FAR RIGHT
West of Samarkand: the 12th-century minaret (known as the Tower of Death) in Bukhara, Uzbekistan

BELOW (from left to right)
Wu Man, Wu Tong and Joel Fan: the *pipa*, *sheng* and piano soloists in the Silk Road Ensemble and, with Yo-Yo Ma on cello, in Bright Sheng's quadruple concerto *The Song and Dance of Tears*

Cyla von Tiedemann (below); T. Waltham/Robert Harding Picture Library (far right) Elizabeth ten Grotenhuis (right)

aspirants. And by enlisting musicologist Ted Levin – the supreme authority on Central Asia's nomad musics – Ma ensured that his team would be the right stuff.

Levin went on a trawl through the local conservatories, fended off the star pupils who were thrust at him, and sought out young musicians with open minds and collaborative instincts; he commissioned local composers to create works blending Eastern and Western instruments. As Levin points out, this was to be a restitution: 500 years ago, under the Pax Mongolica, Central Asia was humming with creativity – the antithesis to the forgotten backwater oppressed by the dead weight of the former Soviet Union.

I first caught up with the Silk Road Project three years ago in, of all places, Schleswig-Holstein. The compositions they paraded there – now available on Sony's *Silk Road Journeys* disc – were dazzling proof that the experiment was a success. After a triumphant visit to the 2002 Smithsonian Folklife Festival – at which American politicos scrambled to leap on this suddenly fashionable bandwagon – Ma's plan was to tour the Central Asian 'Stans' (Kazakhstan, Kyrgyzstan, Tajikistan, *etc.*), but the Afghan war put paid to that. He's always made it scrupulously clear that the project won't play politics – indeed, it offers a wonderfully civilised alternative – but there's no countering the fact that the fiddle can't compete with the gun.

Last spring the Silk Road Ensemble did make it to the 'Stans', and it was heart-warming to watch them wow the crowds in Almaty, Bishkek and war-torn

PROM 38

Bright Sheng (b. 1955)
The Song and Dance of Tears • UK premiere

Born in Shanghai in 1955, Bright Sheng began learning the piano at the age of 4. As a result, instead of being sent to work in the fields during the Cultural Revolution, he was sent to work for seven and a half years as a pianist with a folk music troupe in the remote province of Qinghai, near Tibet. After the Revolution, he studied composition at the Shanghai Conservatory, before moving to New York in 1982, when he found a mentor in the late Leonard Bernstein. But it is Bartók whom he cites as his main model in attempting to meld Chinese and Western styles. Four years ago, he returned to China to spend two months collecting folk music along the route of the ancient Silk Road. *The Song and Dance of Tears* is not, he says, 'an attempt to recreate the scenes and music I heard on the trip' but 'an evocation of the impressions and emotions that stayed with me deeply'. Featuring four soloists – on *pipa* (a lute-like instrument first brought into China along the Silk Road over 2,000 years ago), *sheng* (a Chinese mouth organ that is arguably the ancestor of both the Western organ and accordion), cello and piano – Bright's 'tone poem' was premiered by the New York Philharmonic in March 2003. Three of the Silk Road Ensemble soloists from that performance – Wu Tong (*sheng*), Wu Man (*pipa*) and Yo-Yo Ma (cello) – will be playing it again at the 2004 Proms, plus Joel Fan (piano).

ABOVE
Bright Sheng, taking a camel ride along the old Silk Road in the summer of 2000

BELOW
Kayhan Kalhor, the Iranian composer/*kemancheh*-player

Dushanbe, where Ma was formally granted honorary Tajikhood. It certainly helped that they could field stars of the calibre of Iranian spike-fiddler Kayhan Kalhor, Azerbaijani praise-singer Alem Qasimov, Chinese *pipa*-player Wu Man, and the breathtaking Mongolian diva Ganbaatar Khongorzul.

But the big thrill lay in seeing how the Ensemble's creations now constitute a genre, with none of the fakery normally associated with the word 'fusion'. It is of course fusion, when the *pipa* mates with the cello, and the violin underpins the soaring sound of a *maqam* singer, but this kind is genuinely organic. Now at last, thanks to the BBC Proms, London is being let in on the act.

The Silk Road Ensemble at the Proms

PROM 38	Bright Sheng *The Song and Dance of Tears* Messiaen *Turangalîla Symphony*
PROM 40	To include: Zhao Jiping *Moon over Guan Mountains*, Sandeep Das *Tarang*, Kayhan Kalhor *Blue as the Turquoise Night of Neyshabur*, and arrangements of Armenian folk songs and music of the Roma
PCM 5	To include: Jia da Qun *Prospect of Colored Desert*, Debussy *Cello Sonata*, Kayhan Kalhor *Gallop of 1,000 Horses*, music for solo *pipa*

For details of the British Library's Silk Road exhibition, see pages 142–3

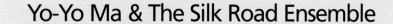

Yo-Yo Ma & The Silk Road Ensemble

Silk Road Journeys

When Strangers Meet

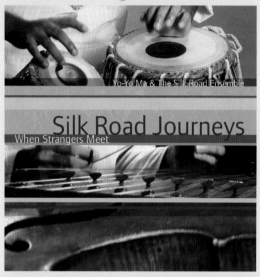

The Silk Road Project explores the rich cultural traditions that flourished along the Silk Road, the historic link between the peoples of Europe and Asia. The new recording introduces The Silk Road Ensemble, a collective of over a dozen like-minded musicians dedicated to exploring the relationship between tradition and innovation in music from the East and West. Yo-Yo Ma joins the ensemble on each track of the recording, which features newly created and traditional works from Asian and Middle Eastern composers that bring together Eastern and Western musical traditions.

SK 89782

℗ Sony Classical, 10 Great Marlborough Street, London, W1F 7LP

www.sonyclassical.com
www.silkroadproject.org

The Choir of The Temple Church

Does your talented son enjoy singing?

Would he enjoy the musical and educational opportunities to be found as a chorister, singing week-by-week in London's beautiful Temple Church?

Would you like him to live at home, attend the City of London School from the age of 10 and have individual singing tuition?

All choristers receive a generous bursary to the City of London School – in some cases to cover 100% of the fees.

Recent and new highlights for a chorister of the Temple Church

- Tour of Brazil
- Mahler, Symphony of a Thousand, Royal Albert Hall
- Elgar, Dream of Gerontius, Royal Festival Hall
- Tavener, The Veil of the Temple, world-premières of Sir John's All-Night Vigil commissioned for the Choir of the Temple Church
- CD, The Tavener Collection, Decca
- Tavener, The Veil of the Temple, USA-première of the All-Night Vigil at the Lincoln Center Festival, Avery Fisher Hall, New York, 24 July 2004
- Tavener, The Veil of the Temple, world-première of the composer's Concert Version at the BBC Proms, Royal Albert Hall, 1 August 2004

STEPHEN LAYTON, M.A., F.R.C.O. Director of Music
JAMES VIVIAN, M.A., F.R.C.O. Organist

An exciting future schedule includes concerts, foreign tours and broadcasts.

Stephen Layton and James Vivian would be pleased to hear your son sing after his seventh birthday. For auditions please contact:

The Music Department
The Temple Church, The Master's House, Temple, EC4Y 7BB
Liz Clarke 020 7353 8559
pa@templechurch.com

www.templechurch.com
www.theveilofthetemple.com

KEF UNI-Q® LOUDSPEAKERS

eXQuisite

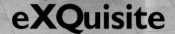

If you're into sound, there's huge pleasure to be had from wideband formats like SACD and DVD-A. But to get the full benefit, you need a bit more than the same old speaker technology in a square wooden box.

That's where the new XQ Series comes in. Sure, they look the part – but what makes them so special is how they perform. The illusion of presence they create is so real it's scary. The detailing is phenomenal, wherever you sit - even at super audio frequencies. We're talking total immersion in a way that's simply not possible with conventional systems.

No wonder – the XQ is packed with high end technologies from the latest Reference Series, including KEF's radical new Hypertweeter™ and the most sophisticated UNI-Q® arrays ever made. Hardware that changes your pulse rate.

Please yourself.

www.kef.com/xq

UNI-Q® TECHNOLOGY

KEF XQ SERIES

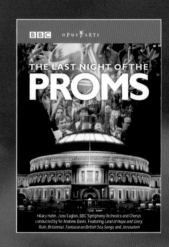

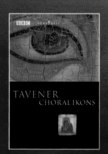

Northern Sinfonia

Music Director **Thomas Zehetmair**

Photo: Keith Pattison

"Why is no other orchestra doing anything even half as interesting as this?"
The Guardian - November 2003

"a consistently superb and crisp performance that bristled with energy and excitement."
The Scotsman - August 2003

"This is the sort of stimulating brew that is fast becoming one of the hallmarks of the Sinfonia's programming policy under its new music director, Thomas Zehetmair."
Daily Telegraph - July 2003

"pure energy from start to finish"
The Times - July 2003

The Sage Gateshead – Northern Sinfonia's new home and international centre for music and musical discovery – due to open this winter.

www.thesagegateshead.org   0191 443 4666

BOHEMIA

BACK TO

Music of the woods and fields

As we celebrate a wealth of anniversaries, including those of Heinrich Biber, Antonín Dvořák and Leoš Janáček, Jan Smaczny reveals how our expanding knowledge of Czech repertoire has given us access to a whole new world of musical riches

Only two generations ago, the prevailing image of Czech music was founded largely on a handful of symphonies by Dvořák, his *Slavonic Dances* and his Cello Concerto. To this base might be added variously the two most popular numbers from Smetana's patriotic cycle *Má vlast*, 'Vltava' and 'From Bohemia's Woods and Fields', the overture and dances from his opera *The Bartered Bride* and, if an orchestra could afford the extra brass, Janáček's *Sinfonietta*. Much has changed since then. The arrival of Janáček's mature operas in the western repertoire has vastly extended an appetite for Czech music, including Janáček's own chamber, keyboard and orchestral works; the availability of a much larger range of Dvořák's output and a growing knowledge of the music of Bohuslav Martinů, Josef Suk and Vítězslav Novák have also augmented the public's appreciation of this vast Central European storehouse of musical riches.

Extending our knowledge of Czech music forwards, to major contemporary luminaries such as Petr Eben (who celebrated his 75th birthday in January), and backwards, from Smetana and Dvořák to the likes of Vejvanovský, Biber and

Zelenka, raises the question of tradition, and tradition there certainly was, both among composers and performers. The guardians of Czech chamber and concert music in the 20th century comprise a line of great string quartets and, of course, the Czech Philharmonic Orchestra. Both branches of endeavour had close connections with Dvořák. Founded in 1892, the Czech Quartet included Oskar Nedbal (viola) and Josef Suk (second violin): both composition pupils of Dvořák, they provided a benchmark of international excellence for the many other Czech quartets of the last century. The origins of the Czech Philharmonic also have strong Dvořák connections. As an orchestral viola player during his twenties, Dvořák knew many of Prague's practising musicians well and played regularly under Smetana's conductorship at the Provisional Theatre. Although he was not always complimentary about performing standards in Prague, or its concert halls, he took the baton for the founding concert of the Czech Philharmonic on 4 January 1896, conducting the 'New World' Symphony among other of his works. At this year's Proms the CPO

returns the compliment by performing the same symphony, plus the *Scherzo capriccioso* and the Violin Concerto – all under the baton of revered Czech specialist, Sir Charles Mackerras – on the exact anniversary of the composer's birthday.

In the cases of Dvořák, Smetana and Janáček, the connections were largely ones of acquaintance and spiritual affinity. But there was also a strongly dynastic aspect to the Czech musical tradition. Given the tendency for both amateur and professional musicianship to run within families in Bohemia and Moravia, it would have been surprising, indeed, had Dvořák not come from a musical background. He counted a trumpeter and violinist among his uncles, and his father was, for a time quite probably professionally, a zither player. While Dvořák, of course, massively transcended these humble roots, his later family had strong links in Prague's musical circles. His wife Anna, who had sung as a child at the Provisional Theatre, was a more than reliable alto and often took solos in performances in Prague; and all of their children were musical. The key event that engendered perhaps the best-known Czech musical dynasty of the 20th century was the marriage, in 1898, of Dvořák's daughter Otilie to his pupil Josef Suk (1874–1935). Composers and performers duly emerged from the Suk line in the succeeding generations and Dvořák's great-grandson, another Josef Suk (born 1929), has enjoyed a long career as a fine solo violinist and conductor.

The dynastic impulse had deep roots in Czech musical and social history. During the 18th and 19th centuries, there was hardly a musician of note in the Czech lands who did not come from a family in which music was practised professionally. Mozart's rival, Leopold Kozeluch, and

Beethoven's boyhood friend, Antoine Reicha (Antonín Rejcha), both came from musical tribes.

Significantly, while Prague was the centre to which most musicians of note were drawn, very few major composers were actually born in the capital. In a sense, this has much to do with the nature of musical education in Bohemia and Moravia. As part of a programme of cultural, as well as political and linguistic, domination following the defeat of Czech forces at the Battle of the White Mountain in 1620, the Austrian crown fostered an extensive network of Jesuit colleges and seminaries in both the countryside and Prague itself. In many ways these acted as finishing schools for young musicians who had also benefited from excellent tuition at village level. Many of the most significant names in Czech music of the

17th and 18th centuries were recipients of this musical bounty, among them Pavel Josef Vejvanovský (c1633–93), Jan Dismas Zelenka (1679–1745) and Josef Mysliveček (1737–81). But, as the 18th-century music historian Charles Burney could not resist pointing out, opportunities for Czech musicians to work at home were limited, so when 'a man of genius among them becomes an admirable musician … he generally runs away, and settles in some other country, where he can enjoy the fruit of his talents'. Thus we see Zelenka making a living in Dresden and Mysliveček flourishing as an opera composer in Italy, where he soon became known as 'Il boemo' (The Bohemian) and later provided a stylistic model for the young Mozart, whom he met and befriended in Bologna in 1770.

Vejvanovský was an exception to this pattern. Having studied at the Jesuit college in Opava, he entered the service of the Prince-Bishop of Olomouc (Olmütz) at his splendid summer palace in the Moravian town of Kroměříž, where he wrote much church music and some distinctive instrumental works, often featuring his own instrument, the trumpet.

The connections between noble establishments in the Czech lands during this period often benefited musicians in terms of employment and mobility. The north Bohemian village of Wartenberg, where Heinrich Biber was born in 1644, was part of the estate of Count Maximilian Liechtenstein-Castelcorno, brother to the equally sensationally-named Karl, Prince-Bishop of Olomouc. Thus was established the link that brought the

ABOVE
Josef Mysliveček, 'Il boemo': a portrait presumably painted before 1778, when he had his nose burnt off during VD treatment in Munich

BELOW
Bedřich Smetana

PCM 6

Heinrich Biber (1644–1704)
Mystery (Rosary) Sonatas Nos. 1, 6 & 10

As well as being one of the finest composers for the violin of the late 17th century, Biber *(inset)* was also perhaps the most imaginative in his attempts to expand the range of violin sonority. In several of his works he asks for the instrument's strings to be specially retuned – a technique, known as *scordatura*, which is used in all but one of the sonatas that he composed around 1674 and based on the 15 Mysteries of the Rosary. The exception is the first of the set, which tells the story of the Annunciation of the birth of Christ: as befits the solemnity of the occasion, a sober prelude introduces a group of variations of ever-increasing brilliance. The sixth and tenth sonatas, 'The Agony in the Garden' and 'The Crucifixion', belong to the Mysteries of Sorrow. Both are solemn meditations whose intensity is enhanced by the *scordatura*. In Biber's evocation of the Crucifixion, however, pain is transcended by victory – a victory depicted in the richest sonorities.

Antonín Dvořák (1841–1904)
The Spectre's Bride

Following his triumphant first visit to England in 1884, during which he conducted his *Stabat mater* at the Royal Albert Hall, Dvořák was commissioned to write new choral works for both the Birmingham and Leeds festivals. The first of these was *The Spectre's Bride*, the British premiere of which he conducted in Birmingham in 1885. Based on a ballad derived from Czech folklore, it tells the tale of a hapless maiden whose ex-lover returns from the dead to claim her but who is saved, after a rapturous prayer to the Virgin, by the timely arrival of dawn. The macabre plot may well have played some part in the cantata's success with Victorian audiences. But, as with his 1882 grand opera *Dimitrij* (Prom 3), whose plot begins almost exactly where Musorgsky's *Boris Godunov* leaves off, Dvořák's response to the drama of the text results in a consistently gripping musical canvas, with vivid orchestral colours, sweeping choruses and, at its heart, a magnificent duet for the girl and the spectre.

Bedřich Smetana (1824–84)
Má vlast – selection

Smetana's *Má vlast* (My Country) is about place and space. Having given the Czechs a series of national operas with which they could identify (from *The Brandenburgers in Bohemia* and *The Bartered Bride* to *Dalibor* and *Libuše*), Smetana decided during the 1870s to commemorate his nation's history, mythology and landscape in purely orchestral terms. As a committed follower of Liszt, the obvious medium was a series of programmatic symphonic poems (six in all). In 'Vyšehrad', named after the ancient stronghold of Prague, we are drawn into a mythic world in which the triumphs and disasters of the Czech nation are reviewed in music that ranges from exultation to elegy. 'From Bohemia's Woods and Fields' and 'Vltava' both celebrate the beauties of the Czech landscape. The progress of the river Vltava from its source to Prague is captured in a series of evocative episodes swept along by an unforgettable main melody, while 'From Bohemia's Woods and Fields' celebrates the majesty and joy of the countryside, in the shape of a polka.

ABOVE RIGHT
The False Dmitry: the renegade Orthodox monk who reigned as Tsar for a year after invading Russia in 1605 with the help of Polish troops, claiming to be Ivan the Terrible's long-lost son

ABOVE
The Spectre's Bride: title page of the original score

BELOW RIGHT
View of the Vltava: coloured etching after a painting by Lorenz Janscha (1749–1812)

24-year-old Biber to Kroměříž, where he worked as a violinist in the Kapelle, under the supervision of Vejvanovský. Two years later, however, Biber jumped ship to a still more glorious establishment, that of Maximilian Gandolph von Khuenburg, Archbishop of Salzburg, though he continued to send manuscripts back to his old friends in Kroměříž, including that of what is perhaps his best-known piece, the 1673 military sonata, *Battalia*.

Although the Jesuit colleges were long gone by the time of Dvořák (1841–1904) and Janáček (1854–1928), they both benefited from an educational background similar in many ways to their 18th-century predecessors. In each case, modest, though estimable, rural beginnings were refined in an institute of higher learning: both attended the Prague Organ School, founded in 1830 to bolster standards in church music, and drank from the well of Baroque technique with

nary a word about Wagner or even sonata form. The impact of this education was particularly marked in the case of Dvořák, who remained throughout his career an avid sketcher in figured bass and a frequent user of Baroque figures, particularly in his choral music.

The fact that the excellently-trained Dvořák and Janáček remained in their native land, rather than seeking work abroad like so many of their 17th- and 18th-century predecessors, had much to do with a quickening of musical life at home and, above all, the creation of a native Czech school of opera. It is worth remembering, however, that, while Dvořák's famous expedition to the 'New World' was made not out of frustration with local conditions but from a

PROM 16

Leoš Janáček (1854–1928)
Glagolitic Mass

It appears that the *Glagolitic Mass* arose in part from a conversation that Janáček *(above)* had with a senior churchman on the falling standards of Czech church music. Picking up the gauntlet of his challenge to improve the situation, Janáček decided to make a setting of the Mass in Old Church Slavonic. But rather than evoking the solemnity of a church, Janáček's act of worship seems to take place out of doors, among the forests and hills of his native Moravia. Like the near-contemporary *Sinfonietta* (Prom 32) – his largest purely orchestral score, and a work intended to convey his love both for his adopted city of Brno and for the new Czechoslovak state founded in the wake of the First World War – the *Glagolitic Mass* begins with inspirational fanfares, before proceeding to explore the text in a characteristically original way. The start of the 'Gloria', for example, is rapt rather than raucous, while the focus of the resurrection section of the 'Credo' is on mystery rather than celebration. Not surprisingly, the world of Janáček's late operas, and of the forest fantasy *The Cunning Little Vixen* in particular, is rarely far away in this inspiring, outdoor work.

desire for greater financial security, Bedřich Smetana (1824–84) did in fact emigrate to Sweden for five years in his early thirties – 'Prague did not wish to acknowledge me,' he wrote home to his parents, 'so I left it'. And indeed he might never have returned but for the opening, in 1862, of the Provisional Theatre, the precursor of the National Theatre that now stands on the banks of the Vltava (the river whose course he so graphically depicted in his symphonic cycle *Má vlast*). Modest as it was, the Provisional Theatre nevertheless provided the focus for the national revival and any composer who wished to make his mark from then on had to compose opera. Dvořák did this with a will, composing a total of 11, six in the 1870s alone. Understanding a composer means understanding the traditions they served and grew out of; thus ignoring, as we are

still inclined to do, Dvořák's work as an opera composer (*Rusalka* alone excepted) fatally undermines a true appreciation of what motivated him. This season's rare performance of *Dimitrij*, surely the finest of Dvořák's grand operas, should help restore the balance.

With Leoš Janáček, arguably the most original Czech composer of all time, understanding the traditions that underpinned his development shows how fruitfully he reacted against them. When Janáček, like many of his Czech contemporaries, turned to realist opera in the 1890s, his reaction to that particular tradition produced, in *Jenůfa*, one of the signal masterpieces of the genre, but one that is a long way from the simple melodic conventions of the style.

Bohuslav Martinů (1890–1959) fits remarkably well into this tradition, even if his true finishing school was not the Prague Conservatoire, from which he was

PROM 18

Bohuslav Martinů (1890–1959)
The Frescoes of Piero della Francesca

Ever since his childhood, much of which was spent gazing down from the church tower where his family lived, Martinů took a keen interest in the world around him. Travelling in northern Italy in the spring of 1955, he was captivated by a recently uncovered fresco of the Resurrection by Piero della Francesca, and prompted to visit the more extensive frescoes depicting 'The Story of the True Cross' in Arezzo. The musical result was effectively a miniature three-movement symphony that evokes Piero's world of colour, simplicity and beauty. The opening of the work has something of the numinous quality of Martinů's Sixth Symphony (*Fantaisies symphoniques*) of 1953, but no single mood lasts for long in this arresting, ever-changing score. Predominantly tonal in idiom, though never banal, the music seems to be suggesting the response of a mind viewing Piero's frescoes, rather than an attempt at literal illustration.

ABOVE
The Dream of Constantine:
one of the frescoes from the 'True Cross' cycle by Piero della Francesca (c1420–92) that Martinů saw in Arezzo

ABOVE
Bohuslav Martinů

expelled (for 'incorrigible negligence'), but Paris, where he lived from 1923 to 1940. His trajectory, from village to big city, has clear resemblances to his Czech predecessors, although his decision to live mainly abroad (apart from holidays and attendance at pre-war premieres, he never returned to his native land) was more in the manner of the Czech musicians of the 18th rather than the 19th century. But it is in his method of composing that he

proclaims his origins. Apart from a formidable technique that allowed him to make almost any compositional impulse in almost any genre a concrete reality, he joyed in the use of small, quasi-Baroque figures and frequently approached 18th-century ways of structuring works, notably in the Double Concerto for two string orchestras, piano and timpani, written for Paul Sacher's Basle orchestra in 1938. Like Janáček

and a number of 18th- and early 19th-century composers, Martinů made occasional use of Czech folk material. But if the use of native material is a common factor that emerges from time to time among Czech composers, it should not be read as a primary colour; the enduring strength of Czech musical tradition is based on an underlying technical strength that is always present in the finest of its products.

Czech music at the Proms

Biber	Battalia	Prom 26		Eben	Sunday music – Moto ostinato	Prom 48
	Missa bruxellensis	Prom 35				
	Mystery (Rosary) Sonatas:			Janáček	Glagolitic Mass	Prom 16
	No. 1 'The Annunciation';				Hukvaldy Songs	Prom 16
	No. 6 'The Agony in the Garden';				Taras Bulba	Prom 18
	No. 10 'The Crucifixion'	PCM 6			Sinfonietta	Prom 32
					The Eternal Gospel	Prom 36
Dvořák	Dimitrij	Prom 3			Our Father	Prom 48
	Mass in D major	Prom 13			String Quartet No. 1, 'Kreutzer Sonata'	PCM 1
	Czech Suite	Prom 15			In the Mists	PCM 4
	Symphony No. 8 in G major	Prom 19			Concertino	PCM 8
	Symphony No. 6 in D major	Prom 25				
	Cello Concerto in B minor	Prom 29		Martinů	Double Concerto	Prom 7
	The Spectre's Bride	Prom 32			The Frescoes of Piero della Francesca	Prom 18
	Wind Serenade	Prom 34			La revue de cuisine	PCM 8
	Legend in G minor, Op. 59 No. 3	Prom 53				
	Serenade for strings	Prom 53		Mysliveček	L'Olimpiade – 'Che non mi disse un di!'	Prom 7
	Slavonic Dance in E minor, Op. 72 No. 2	Prom 53				
	Symphony No. 7 in D minor	Prom 66		Novák	Melancholic Songs of Love	Prom 7
	Scherzo capriccioso	Prom 70				
	Symphony No. 9, 'From the New World'	Prom 70		Smetana	Má vlast – 'Vyšehrad'; 'From Bohemia's Woods and Fields'; 'Vltava'	Prom 31
	Violin Concerto in A minor	Prom 70				
	Rusalka – 'Song to the Moon'	Prom 73				
	The Water Goblin	Prom 73		Vejvanovský	Sonata vespertina a 8	Prom 7
	Overture 'Carnival'	Prom 74				
	Piano Quintet in A major, Op. 81	PCM 1		Zelenka	Ouverture a 7; Concerto a 8	Prom 26
	Moravian Duets – selections	PCM 3				

FESTIVAL 2004 15 August - 5 September

et your summer alight in Edinburgh with a sizzling three weeks of opera, music, theatre and dance.

What they said in 2003:

There were not enough hours in the day'
estival-goer

This was real International Festival stuff -
nd it made you glad to be alive'
he Mail on Sunday

Exactly the sort of thing you hope for from
n international festival - challenging,
angerous, compelling and exhilarating'
The Times

Abandon your routine and your sanity
nd feast upon the cultural smorgasbord'
he Independent

A dizzying array of the world's greatest and most innovative artists and companies include Hanover State Opera performing Debussy's Pelléas et Mélisande, Verdi's Il Trovatore and Nono's Al Gran sole carico d'amore. Operas in concert include Weber's Der Freischütz, Oberon and Euryanthe. Orchestras include The Cleveland Orchestra, Leipzig Gewandhaus, Dresden Staatskapelle and Ensemble Intercontemporain; recitals by Violeta Urmana, Richard Goode, Elisabeth Leonskaya, Leonidas Kavakos. And with glorious chamber music every morning, classic theatre, new writing, contemporary dance and classical ballet, there's more than enough for culture vultures and first time visitors alike.

SPARK YOUR IMAGINATION
o book or for a free brochure
all 0131 473 2000
r visit www.eif.co.uk

EDINBURGH
INTERNATIONAL
FESTIVAL

TUNE IN TO THE WORLD'S KNOWLEDGE

www.bl.uk

THE BRITISH LIBRARY SOUND ARCHIVE

One of the largest sound archives in the world, the collection includes over a million commercial discs, off-air radio broadcasts, private recordings, interviews and documentaries about music and musicians. The Sound Archive is an invaluable resource for professional and amateur musicians, researchers, teachers and broadcasters.

■ Edison Visiting Fellowships for intensive research with recordings
■ Free Listening & Viewing Service (by appointment)
■ Poets and authors in their own words published on CD
■ Audio-rich web pages illustrating spoken word, music and wildlife collections
■ The Saul Seminars on music and sound recording.

96 Euston Road London NW1
T +44 (0)20 7412 7676
F +44 (0)20 7412 7441
sound-archive@bl.uk

The British Library's Exhibition Galleries are open 7 days a week and are free of charge.

THE SILK ROAD Trade, Travel, War and Faith
7 May – 12 September 2004

in collaboration with THE BRITISH MUSEUM

A once in a lifetime opportunity to view rarely seen Silk Road treasures excavated by the explorer Aurel Stein. Take our journey eastwards from Samarkand to the borders of ancient China. Find out about the ordinary and extraordinary people who lived along the Silk Road in the first millennium AD and decide how much life has really changed in 1000 years.

Deepen your experience of the Silk Road through:
■ Free Gallery talks highlighting different aspects of the Silk Road Exhibition
■ Sounds of the Silk Road in the Gallery
■ Stein's own photographs of the Silk Road (from June)
■ A contemporary fashion display (from August).

John Ritblat Gallery: Treasures of the British Library original musical score of Handel's Messiah and other original works by Beethoven, Chopin, Bach, The Beatles and many more on permanent display.

EDUCATING
THE MUSICIANS OF TOMORROW

Do you know a child with a special talent in music?

The UK's five specialist music schools exist to provide a unique world-class education.

Come and visit us

St Mary's Music School,
Coates Hall, 25 Grosvenor Crescent,
Edinburgh EH12 5EL
Tel. 0131 538 7766
www.st-marys-music-school.co.uk

Chethams School of Music,
Long Millgate,
Manchester M3 1SB
Tel. 0161 834 9644
www.chethams.com

The Purcell School,
Aldenham Road,
Bushey, Herts WD23 2TS
Tel. 01923 331100
www.purcell-school.org

Yehudi Menuhin School,
Cobham Road, Stoke d'Abernon,
Cobham, Surrey KT11 3QQ
Tel. 01932 864739
www.yehudimenuhinschool.co.uk

Wells Cathedral School,
Wells, Somerset
BA5 2ST
Tel. 01749 834200
www.wells-cathedral-school.com

Government funding is available for UK residents providing up to 100% of fees.

Visit the DfES website: www.dfes.gov.uk/mds for more information about the music and dance scheme.

NAMDS
THE NATIONAL ASSOCIATION
OF MUSIC AND DANCE SCHOOLS

PHOTOGRAPHY MIKE HOBAN

GLYNDEBOURNE
ON TOUR
2004

G PUCCINI
LA BOHÈME
A revival of David McVicar's production, premiered in 2000.

W A MOZART
DIE ZAUBERFLÖTE
A new production by Adrian Noble, premiered at the 2004 Festival.

C DEBUSSY
PELLÉAS ET MÉLISANDE
A revival of Graham Vick's production, premiered in 1999.

GLYNDEBOURNE	5 – 23 October
WOKING	26 – 30 October
MILTON KEYNES	2 – 6 November
NORWICH	9 – 13 November
PLYMOUTH	16 – 20 November
STOKE-ON-TRENT	23 – 27 November
OXFORD	30 November – 4 December

To join our FREE mailing list and receive full details of the 2004 Tour,
please call 01273 815 000 or email info@glyndebourne.com or write to:
GOT Mailing List, Freepost BR (235), Glyndebourne, Lewes, East Sussex BN8 4BR

www.glyndebourne.com

'GLYNDEBOURNE ON TOUR ...
A YOUTHFUL AND VIBRANT JOURNEY'
Sunday Independent 2000

ARTS COUNCIL
ENGLAND

1934

ENGLAND AT THE CROSSROADS

A changing musical landscape

Stephen Johnson looks back 70 years and finds a surprising amount of common ground between the five major English composers who came and went in 1934

It could be synchronicity, or just plain coincidence, but the year 1934 is a crucial date in the history of English music. This was the year in which three of the great patriarchs of the English musical renaissance died, and two of our most important and internationally celebrated living composers were born. It was also the year in which a certain Benjamin Britten turned 21 – a fact that would have been a lot less noteworthy if he hadn't already been attracting attention as a composer. 1934 also saw the sensationally successful premiere of the (still incomplete) First Symphony by the 32-year-old William Walton, and the completion of another symphony that was to be just as enthusiastically received when it was heard the following year, Vaughan Williams's Fourth – its violent modernism marking an invigorating new development for a composer already in his sixties.

PROM 1

Edward Elgar (1857–1934)
The Music Makers

It was in the choral ode *The Music Makers*, along with the Violin Concerto and the Second Symphony, that Elgar claimed he had 'written out my soul'. In these works, rather than in the rousingly populist *Cockaigne* or *Pomp and Circumstance* Marches, one encounters the private Elgar: complex, prone to emotional extremes, a different creature entirely from the 'glad, confident' Bard of Empire once widely portrayed. In *The Music Makers* Elgar makes intriguing use of self-quotations from several of his earlier works, including *The Dream of Gerontius*, *Sea Pictures*, the First Symphony and the *Enigma Variations*. In connection with Arthur O'Shaughnessy's verses, these familiar themes reveal new, possibly more private meanings. As Elgar explained, he used the 'Enigma' theme 'because it expressed when written (in 1898) my sense of the loneliness of the artist as described in the first six lines of the ode'. For anyone who wants to understand Elgar better, *The Music Makers* is essential listening.

TOP LEFT
Sir Peter Maxwell Davies in Antarctica

LEFT
Young Elgar on the Malvern Hills: image from Ken Russell's 1962 *Monitor* biography

RIGHT
Edward Elgar with Marco, his pet spaniel

ABOVE
The Elgar memorial window in Worcester Cathedral

So there were good reasons to be hopeful about the future of English music in 1934. The losses were, nevertheless, significant. First, on 23 February, Edward Elgar died. Elgar's historical position as the first composer of truly international importance in British music since Henry Purcell's death in 1695 was secure enough, but the reputation of much of his music was at a low ebb. While the rumbustious concert overture *Cockaigne* was still popular, and it would have taken a revolution to dislodge the *Enigma Variations* from its place in the popular repertoire, works such as the Violin Concerto and the choral ode *The Music Makers* – works in which Elgar claimed he had 'written out my soul' – were far from widely appreciated. Part of Elgar's problem in his last years was that many saw him as an anachronism, a relic of a vanished past – of the seemingly 'innocent' confidence of Edwardian England that had been destroyed by the experience of the First World War. In his darker moments the hyper-self-critical Elgar was inclined to judge himself in similar terms, especially since the years after the war had brought a marked falling-off in the quantity and quality of his output. Which is one of the reasons why Anthony Payne's magnificent 'elaboration' of the sketches for Elgar's uncompleted Third Symphony (originally a BBC commission) was greeted with such enthusiasm by so many Elgarians. It shows that, in these final years, the composer's creative flame was burning as brightly as ever; and that, if the rapid onset of his fatal illness hadn't prevented him from completing it, Elgar's Third might well have been greeted with the same enthusiasm as Walton's First and Vaughan Williams's Fourth – a trinity of great English symphonies.

The death of Elgar at 76 was sad but hardly surprising. The death of the 59-year-old Gustav Holst on 25 May was more of a shock – not least to Holst's close friend Vaughan Williams, who despite his long experience keenly felt the loss of Holst's advice and encouragement. In 1934, as today, Holst was internationally celebrated for his brilliant orchestral suite *The Planets* – but not for much else. Although his choral-orchestral masterpiece *The Hymn of Jesus* had been admired at its premiere in 1920,

---

PROM 14

Elgar, 'elaborated' by Anthony Payne (b. 1936)
Symphony No. 3

In an extraordinary act of dedication and creative daring, the composer Anthony Payne took the extensive sketches for the BBC-commissioned symphony that Elgar was still working on at the time of his death and 'elaborated' them into a complete 55-minute score. In so doing, Payne proved that the received view of the sketches – that they show Elgar's powers in sad decline – was simply wrong. The first and third movements are especially impressive: the one an energetic, sweeping Allegro movement based on the interplay of two splendid themes, the other a darkly-moving slow movement worthy to stand beside the great adagios of the First and Second Symphonies. Elgar left no clue as to how his Third Symphony might end; but during a sleepless night in an American hotel Payne was suddenly struck by the idea of combining the finale theme with the regular repeating rhythmic pattern of Elgar's orchestral miniature 'The Wagon Passes', from his *Nursery Suite*. The result is a conclusion that feels both emotionally powerful and musically logical.

LEFT
Elgar's daughter Carice Blake entrusts her late father's sketches for the unfinished Third Symphony to the BBC's music director, Adrian Boult (*left*), and director of programmes, R. H. Eckersley

BELOW
'It seemed as if I was being impelled by forces outside myself': Anthony Payne, whose irresistible urge to 'tinker' with Elgar's sketches has added a new British symphony to the repertoire

PROM 4

Gustav Holst (1874–1934)
The Hymn of Jesus

Composed in 1917, Gustav Holst's *The Hymn of Jesus* is even more radical and forward-looking than *The Planets*, completed a year earlier but still unperformed. Semi-chorus and solo trombone intone free-floating chants through hypnotic repeated patterns for piano and celesta. The main chorus is required to speak one line of the hymn and sing another in weirdly clashing triadic harmonies; later the word 'wisdom' is sung as a hushed whole-tone cluster. But these 'modernist' devices are much more than ear-catching effects. Everything contributes to the strange, unforgettable atmosphere of the whole work, the response of one of this country's most imaginative and intellectually original composers to an enigmatic, almost riddling ancient Christian hymn. Nowhere in this work is there the slightest hint of conventional English choral piety. Holst's fascination with Eastern thought led him to search for a musical language that had nothing to do with European 'developing' models, but rather reflected the timeless qualities of the Byzantine text. The result is one of the high-points of the English choral repertoire.

it had failed to achieve anything like the same popular success as *The Planets*, partly because Holst's Eastward-leaning mysticism was deeply unfashionable in the 1920s and 1930s, but also because it was too technically taxing for all but the most accomplished choirs. Other important works, such as the earlier but equally beautiful and original chamber opera *Sāvitri*, were neglected. But far from being daunted by his 'one-work composer' reputation, Holst had gone on exploring, experimenting with harmony and rhythm, and in the process alienating many British critics.

One could say that Holst remains something of a connoisseur's composer, but as such he still exerts a potent influence. Among living composers, figures as different as Thomas Adès, John Tavener and Harrison Birtwistle have all acknowledged a debt to him, while the example of the *Mahābhārata*-based opera *Sāvitri* was an inspiration to Britten when he came to adapt his first 'church parable', *Curlew River*, from the

Japanese *noh* play *Sumidagawa* (*see also* 'East/West', *pages 4–12*).

Less than a month after the death of Holst, and just over a year after Elgar had visited him at his home in the French village of Grez-sur-Loing, near Fontainebleau, Frederick Delius died on 10 June. Delius is still frequently dismissed as one of the most hopelessly parochial of all English composers – a fact that would probably have had the composer laughing bitterly. Not only was he of German descent on both his maternal and paternal sides, but he graduated from the Leipzig Conservatory and had his first major successes in Germany. The Hungarian composers Béla Bartók and Zoltán Kodály both cited hearing a Viennese performance of Delius's *A Mass of Life* among their formative musical influences – this was in 1911, at a time when Delius was still largely unknown in the land of his birth. By then Delius had settled at Grez, where he was to spend most of the rest of his life. His musical pastorals may have acquired associations

with the English countryside, but most of them found their inspiration elsewhere: the Norwegian uplands, the orange groves of Florida (where Delius had tried to make a living in the late 1880s) or the river at Grez. The ever-popular 'Walk to the Paradise Garden' from the opera *A Village Romeo and Juliet* is set in Switzerland, while the work many

ABOVE RIGHT
Holst at work, correcting parts: portrait (1910) by Millicent Woodforde

ABOVE
Pages from Holst's hand-written composition diary

consider his masterpiece, *Sea Drift*, is a response to a poem set on the Atlantic coast of America. After his death Delius suffered a worse eclipse than Elgar – at least as far as critics and 'serious-minded' composers were concerned. Granted, languid, nostalgic sensuality was never less fashionable than in the decades after the Second World War. Yet Delius's music has refused to fade away, and at least one living English composer – Anthony Payne, completer of Elgar's Third – has admitted to being influenced by him.

Harrison Birtwistle and Peter Maxwell Davies – both born in 1934 (on 15 July and 8 September respectively) and later fellow students at the Royal Manchester College of Music and co-members of the so-called 'Manchester School' – are not names one normally connects with Delius, or with any of the other English pastoralists. Yet, like Delius, Vaughan Williams and Holst, both Birtwistle and Davies are creators of memorable musical landscapes. Birtwistle has acknowledged Holst in particular as an important musical forebear in this respect, and it isn't hard to hear echoes of the repeating, non-developing rhythmic patterns of Holst's *Choral Hymns from the Rig Veda* in Birtwistle's music, or to sense something of the louring atmosphere of Holst's Hardy-inspired *Egdon Heath*. Birtwistle's recent *Theseus Game*, for large ensemble with two conductors, is also a kind of landscape, though the

'scenery' here is the weird nocturnal world of the labyrinth, through which Theseus, ambiguous hero of Greek myth, makes his way, following the thread given to him by the Cretan princess Ariadne. While the writing for the two ensembles is as gritty and astringent as one might expect from Birtwistle, it is the melodic 'thread', divided between different orchestral soloists, that binds *Theseus Game* together and holds the attention. Also featured in this Proms season are four settings of poems by the pianist Alfred Brendel (three of them new), and the choral *Ring Dance of the Nazarene*, composed in the creative wake of the 'dramatic tableau' *The Last Supper*.

Like quite a few other composers of his generation, Peter Maxwell Davies began by defining himself *against* the English romantic pastoral school. Vaughan Williams, for instance, was ridiculed by

Frederick Delius (1862–1934)
Sea Drift

Verses by the American mystical poet Walt Whitman inspired Delius's most moving portrayal of longing and loss, and the work many regard as his masterpiece. In the poem a solitary boy observes a pair of seagulls, and finds himself identifying with the male's anguished cries when the female fails to return: 'O throat! O throbbing heart! And I singing uselessly, uselessly all the night.' Delius's setting goes way beyond nature poetry – though in that respect alone it is impressive. The baritone soloist and chorus tell the story of the gulls' arrival on the shore and fatal separation. Then the baritone sings the gull's lament, while the lush, Wagnerian orchestral writing evokes the 'drift' of the sea as both a vast backdrop to the song and a metaphor for the seeming endlessness of grief. But the end is acceptance, and a kind of serenity.

Sir Harrison Birtwistle (b. 1934)
Theseus Game

In the ancient Greek myth, Theseus is the hero who is able to enter the Labyrinth and slay the half-bull, half-human monster, the Minotaur. He is then able to find his way out again by following the thread given to him by the king's daughter, Ariadne. *Theseus Game* is not a musical portrayal of the legend. Rather, Birtwistle makes the idea of the thread the basis of his argument, as instruments from two ensembles take turns to weave a long, almost continuous melodic line. However dense or spikily dramatic the music thrown out by these ensembles, and however often Birtwistle may pass the melodic line between various soloists (taking their cue from two separate conductors), it is this line that holds centre stage – literally, for this is another of those Birtwistle works (like *Secret Theatre* or the percussion piece *For O, for O, the Hobby-Horse is Forgot*) in which an element of theatre is crucial. The result is an argument that grips the attention throughout its almost 40-minute span.

See also 'New Music', pages 46–51

the young Max for 'dancing on the village green'. Who, in those days, would have guessed that this intense young iconoclast would end up not only conducting Vaughan Williams, as he has on occasion, but also composing a symphony whose very title pays tribute to the older English master? Back in the 1960s, when *Missa super L'homme armé* and *First Fantasia on an 'In nomine' of John Taverner* were written, Maxwell Davies was still searching for antidotes to the influences of the still-recent English musical past in the music of more remote times – in Tudor church and consort music, or in the works of such earlier masters as Guillaume Dufay. This year Prom-goers will be able to compare those early works with the much more recent *Antarctic Symphony* (Symphony No. 8), which, like Vaughan Williams's *Sinfonia antartica*, contains vivid musical portrayals of the sights and sounds of that most remote, un-humanised landscape. Unlike VW, however, Davies wrote his

FAR RIGHT
Sir Harrison Birtwistle with Minotaur sculpture by Beth Carter (property of Mark Glatman)

INSET ABOVE
King Minos's Labyrinth, as depicted on a Cretan coin minted in Knossos in the early 3rd century BC

RIGHT
Ralph Vaughan Williams: friend of Holst, model for Maxwell Davies

symphony in response to direct personal experience, as part of the crew of the scientific research ship RRS *James Clark Ross*. Sounds of breaking ice and avalanches especially impressed Davies, resulting in the creation of 'transmuted

sound images distantly based on those experiences which I hope will evoke in the concert hall listener responses related to mine *in situ*.' In other words, English romanticism lives on!

England at the Crossroads: 1934

Birtwistle	The Ring Dance of the Nazarene	Prom 5
	Theseus Game	Prom 30
	Four Settings of Alfred Brendel	Prom 43
Delius	A Village Romeo and Juliet –	
	The Walk to the Paradise Garden	Prom 2
	Sea Drift	Prom 4
Elgar	The Music Makers	Prom 1
	Cockaigne (In London Town)	Prom 4
	Enigma Variations	Prom 4
	Violin Concerto	Prom 13
	Pomp and Circumstance	
	March No. 1	Prom 74
Elgar/Payne	Symphony No. 3	Prom 14
Holst	The Planets	Prom 1
	The Hymn of Jesus	Prom 4
	Choral Hymns from the Rig Veda	
	(Group 3)	Prom 48
	Sāvitri	Prom 54
Maxwell Davies	First Fantasia on an 'In nomine'	
	of John Taverner	Prom 14
	Antarctic Symphony	Prom 27
	Fantasia on a Ground	
	and Two Pavans (after Purcell)	Prom 71
	Linguae ignis	Prom 71
	Missa super L'homme armé	Prom 71
	Ojai Festival Overture	Prom 74

PROM 27

Sir Peter Maxwell Davies (b. 1934)
Antarctic Symphony (Symphony No. 8)

A recent sea voyage from the Falklands to the Antarctic aboard a scientific research ship inspired Sir Peter Maxwell Davies *(above and right)* to write his *Antarctic Symphony*. Davies was as impressed by some of the sounds he heard as he was by the extraordinary sights: the ice shattering against the bows of the ship as it advanced through frozen seas; and the strange muffled sound of snow falling from ice cliffs on either side of the sea-passage. These dramatic sounds set him thinking of a medieval chant associated with the equally dramatic descent of the Holy Spirit on the Apostles at Pentecost, and so the Eighth Symphony was born. While Davies insists that 'the new symphony cannot be described literally in terms of any programme associated with my Antarctic experience', he freely admits that the drama of the elements, qualities of light, the eerie sense of the slowness of 'the breathing of time' all left their mark on the music, from individual sounds to the shaping and pacing of the 40-minute single-movement structure.

Peter Bucktrout/British Antarctic Survey (main picture); John Batten (inset)

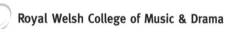

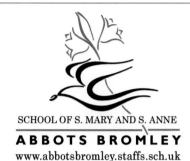

Moving to France made Easy!

Planning your move • Real Estate • Legal • Finance • Insurance
Property Auctions • Leisure Activities • Education • Transport • Shopping
Property to Rent • Earning a Living • Pitfalls and lots, lots MORE...

Membership for the site costs
£24.45 for a month
£61.12 for six months
£107 for a year

Quote 'Proms' to receive an extra

20% off

France Property and Life is on the web at

www.france-property-and-life.com
www.frenchpropertyreport.com

Or alternatively call: 33499 630931

FRANCE
PROPERTY AND LIFE

symphony hall
birmingham

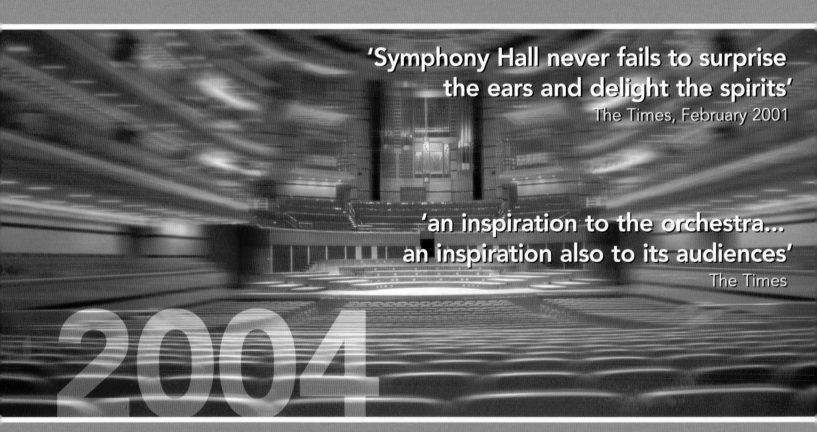

'Symphony Hall never fails to surprise the ears and delight the spirits'
The Times, February 2001

'an inspiration to the orchestra...
an inspiration also to its audiences'
The Times

2004

'The best concert hall in the country'
Daily Telegraph

box office 0121 780 3333

online box office www.symphonyhall.co.uk/boxoffice

www.symphonyhall.co.uk admin tel: +44 (0)121 200 2000

fax: +44 (0)121 212 1982 email: symphonyhall@necgroup.co.uk

NEW MUSIC

MUSIC

NEW

You heard it here first

Since its earliest days, the BBC has always commissioned new music, with Holst and Elgar heading the list of chosen composers. **Anthony Burton** surveys the corporation's proud record of musical patronage; **David Threasher** previews this year's major premieres

ABOVE LEFT
The detonation of the first atom bomb, over the New Mexico desert on 16 July 1945, forms the subject of John Adams's new opera-in-progress, *Doctor Atomic*

LEFT
Orion: the constellation that partly inspired Kaija Saariaho's new piece

ABOVE RIGHT (left to right) John Reith, the BBC's first Director-General; Gustav Holst, the first composer to be commissioned by the new Corporation; Henry Wood, a consistent champion of 'novelties' during his 50 years as conductor of the Proms; William Glock, the Controller of Music who first made the Proms the focus of the BBC's commissioning policy

BELOW RIGHT
Edward Elgar *(right)*, photographed in 1929 with George Bernard Shaw, who three years later persuaded the BBC to commission the composer's Third Symphony

When Elgar began writing his Third Symphony in 1933, it was as a result of personal pressure exercised by the ever-persuasive George Bernard Shaw on the BBC's Director-General, John Reith, to commission it. He was helped by the fact that the principle of BBC commissioning had already been established, with Holst's 1927 choral ballet *The Morning of the Year* heading the list of works brought into being at the behest of the then newly-established Corporation.

Commissioning, however, was only a small part of the BBC's drive to bring modern music to its listening audience, which even in the 1920s included landmark performances of Schoenberg, Stravinsky and Webern, and which was accelerated by the founding in 1930 of the BBC Symphony Orchestra. In the orchestra's impressive list of literally hundreds of British and world premieres, commissions were for many years few and far between, and mostly confined to celebrations of major events. For example, the Coronation of 1937 was marked by Walton's march *Crown Imperial* and John Ireland's cantata *These Things Shall Be*, and the post-war founding of the BBC

Third Programme by Britten's (rapidly withdrawn) *Occasional Overture*.

The BBC's take-over of the Proms in 1927 brought into its fold Henry Wood, a doughty pioneer of new music who had famously given the world premiere of Schoenberg's *Five Pieces for Orchestra* in the 1912 season. Wood remained assiduous in his search for 'novelties', and the annals of the series between 1927 and his death in 1944 include numerous

premieres. But the adventurousness of the Proms was restricted by the BBC's view of them as essentially popular concerts, and the tightness of the rehearsal schedule at a time when the same orchestra played at every concert. The post-war years under Malcolm Sargent brought relatively few important first performances, and no BBC commission was unveiled at the Proms until William Alwyn's overture *Derby Day* in 1960.

The previous year, William Glock had taken over as the BBC's Controller of Music and begun revitalising the Corporation's, and the nation's, musical life. He greatly enlarged the commissioning budget, and focused much of it on the Proms. Among the earliest beneficiaries of this policy were Elisabeth Lutyens, Alexander Goehr and Peter Maxwell Davies (whose breakthrough *First Fantasia on an 'In Nomine' of John Taverner*, commissioned for the 1962 season, is being revived this year). Those who criticise Glock for single-minded devotion to the avant-garde should not overlook the commissions he offered also to very different composers such as Edmund Rubbra and Malcolm Arnold.

The commissioning policy initiated by Glock was maintained by his successors Robert Ponsonby, John Drummond and now Nicholas Kenyon, and has continued to provide the Proms with brand-new works – no fewer than 12 of them in the centenary season of 1995, culminating in Harrison Birtwistle's famous (or rather, notorious) *Panic* on the Last Night.

One more recent beneficiary of a BBC Proms commission is Joseph Phibbs, who wrote *Lumina* for last year's Last Night. He describes a BBC commission as 'a wonderful platform for a young composer, and one that guarantees a very good performance', adding that even for such a sensitive occasion he was encouraged all along 'to write what I wanted to write'. Anthony Payne, the more senior British composer who brought Elgar's sketches for the Third Symphony so memorably to life, has written three of his major orchestral works to Proms commissions – most recently *Visions and Journeys* (winner of the Radio 3 Listeners' Award in the first British Composer Awards) in 2002. A Prommer himself from the age of 14, Payne found it 'incredibly exciting to write a piece for such a huge audience, and for that sensational hall'.

But just as BBC commissions represent only part of Radio 3's continuing commitment to contemporary music, so they are only one component of the new-music mixture at the Proms. As Proms Director Nicholas Kenyon puts it, 'they're balanced up with co-commissions for major projects, such as Birtwistle's *The Ring Dance of the Nazarene* this year, an increasing number of world, British and London premieres of other important new works, such as Henze's 10th Symphony, and revivals of significant recent pieces that deserve a second hearing. It's all about bringing the best of new music to a thoroughly international festival.'

RIGHT (from top to bottom) John Adams, Judith Bingham and Sir Harrison Birtwistle, who all have new pieces being premiered this year

LEFT Joseph Phibbs, whose *Lumina* was premiered at last year's Last Night

PROM 49

John Adams (b. 1947)

Songs of Ragtime and Reminiscence
(Ives, arr. Adams) • UK premiere
Doctor Atomic – 'Easter Eve 1945' • UK premiere
The Dharma at Big Sur • UK premiere

John Adams's relationship with the BBC Symphony Orchestra was strengthened in 2002 when he was made the subject of the orchestra's annual 'Composer Weekend', and formalised last June when he was named Artist in Association to the orchestra – a position 'sufficiently unstructured and flexible,' he has said, 'to allow any number of wild things to happen'. Adams's first 'wild thing' in the post was last summer's *BBC Proms: out & about* project at the Brixton Academy, unpicking the orchestra for a lively audience of 7- to 12-year-olds.

At last year's Proms Adams introduced to the UK the work he had composed in response to the events of 9/11, *On the Transmigration of Souls*. This season he conducts three of his latest scores. New arrangements of songs by Charles Ives reflect his New England upbringing; *The Dharma at Big Sur*, commissioned by the Los Angeles Philharmonic for the new Walt Disney Concert Hall, reflects his sense of spiritual rebirth on first arriving in California from the East; while *Easter Eve 1945* offers a sneak preview of his new opera *Doctor Atomic*, due to open in San Francisco in 2005. Following on from his earlier 'living history' operas, *Nixon in China* and *The Death of Klinghoffer*, *Doctor Atomic* offers a Faustian take on the life of J. Robert Oppenheimer, developer of the first atom bomb.
See also 'East/West', pages 4–12

PROM 48

Judith Bingham (b. 1952)

The Secret Garden
BBC commission: world premiere

Judith Bingham has enjoyed a long and fruitful relationship with the BBC Symphony Chorus – it was the first choir she joined when she came to London to study at the Royal Academy of Music in the early 1970s, and she's written a number of pieces for it, including *Salt in the Blood*, a BBC commission for the centenary season of Proms in 1995. 'I've had some very happy experiences working with them,' enthuses Bingham, 'as they have a high level of engagement with new music and an extremely high technical standard. I'm also delighted to be writing again for Thomas Trotter. He's a wonderfully intelligent and sensitive player. The organ is one of my favourite instruments, always challenging to write for. A great organ like the Albert Hall's is a Pandora's box of possibilities!' Her new work, *The Secret Garden*, 'is about the Garden of Eden after Adam and Eve left. It's been a long-standing idea to do something about the relationship between plants and insects, and about transformation, both in the Christian sense of moving down the stony path of knowledge towards the Kingdom of Heaven, but also in the world of natural synergy: the moth's transformation, the plant's pollination. Most of the piece is set at night, as if in the unconscious, which also points to a psychological transformation. So there are lots of interweaving and subtle themes.'

PROMS 5 & 43

Sir Harrison Birtwistle (b. 1934)

The Ring Dance of the Nazarene
BBC/VARA co-commission:
UK premiere • Prom 5
Four Settings of Alfred Brendel
BBC commission of three new songs:
world premiere • Prom 43

Celebrating his 70th birthday this year, Sir Harrison Birtwistle has developed from being the angry young man of the so-called Manchester School – introducing the innovations of the Darmstadt and Parisian avant-garde into British music, alongside his contemporary, and fellow Manchester student, Sir Peter Maxwell Davies – to being a prolific composer of large-scale works on an international stage. Last season's Proms included the UK premiere of his orchestral work *The Shadow of Night*, a restless meditation on melancholy that provided a rich contrast with the affirmation of Beethoven's 'Choral' Symphony in the same concert.

The Ring Dance of the Nazarene is the latest in a canon of works in which Birtwistle explores ritualistic notions, expressed dramatically in such stage pieces as his Arthurian opera *Gawain* (1991) and his millennial opera-oratorio *The Last Supper* (2000). Working once more with *Gawain*'s librettist, David Harsent, he has created a work centring upon the mystical dancing leader of a pre-Christian sect, set for baritone and chorus with a mixed ensemble of harps, pianos, wind and percussion (including an Iranian drum).

Birtwistle and Alfred Brendel are long-time friends and admirers of each other's work. For the pianist's 70th birthday in 2001, Birtwistle set Brendel's poem 'There is something between us …', and he has now added new settings of three more of the pianist's poems to make up a short cycle that will receive its world premiere at this year's Proms in a concert that will also feature the great poet-pianist's farewell Proms performance, as soloist in Beethoven's 'Emperor' Concerto.
For Birtwistle's 'Theseus Game', see also page 37

PROM 8

John Casken (b. 1949)
Symphony 'Broken Consort'
BBC commission: world premiere

John Casken's association with the Proms goes back to 1986, with BBC commissions including the song-cycle *Still Mine* (1992), the Violin Concerto (1995) and the song-cycle *To the Lovers' Well* (premiered in the 2001 Proms Chamber Music series). His new symphony, *Broken Consort*, has been composed for the BBC Philharmonic, based in Manchester, where he is the University's Professor of Music. As he explains: 'A few members of the orchestra are also expert performers on other instruments, and in non-classical styles of playing. This work is a tribute to their versatility. "Broken consort" is a term sometimes used for a non-homogeneous ensemble in Elizabethan music, but is here used to suggest the presence within the standard concert orchestra of a "gypsy ensemble" comprising cimbalom, piano accordion, electric violin and mandolin. Their tangy sonorities are used to punctuate the orchestral fabric or to weave gypsy-inflected lines through it. One could compare the presence of this "broken consort" within the orchestra to the current situation in the European Union, with its boundaries being extended and the issue of integrating different identities becoming ever more pressing.'

PROM 44

Hans Werner Henze (b. 1926)
Symphony No. 10
UK premiere

No sooner had Henze's Ninth Symphony been unveiled in Berlin in 1997 than he was urged – by the legendary Swiss conductor and musical philanthropist Paul Sacher – to break the Beethovenian 'jinx of the Ninth' and write a tenth symphony. After Sacher's death in 1999, Sir Simon Rattle, a long-time champion of Henze's music, became a second 'muse' for the project. 'I thought of Simon as a Lucifer, a light-bearing angel,' says Henze, 'as a man with a pure and elegant English mind, with subtle hands and the sensory apparatus of a modern man in love with the world.' He describes the Symphony as 'pure nature music – crystalline and clear and English.' It was Rattle who directed the work's world premiere in Lucerne in 2002, but it's another keen champion of Henze who will present its UK premiere at this year's Proms – Ingo Metzmacher, who made his Proms conducting debut with the UK premiere of Henze's Ninth in 2000.

PROM 28

Anders Hillborg (b. 1954)
Exquisite Corpse
UK premiere

The music of the Swedish composer Anders Hillborg, whose 50th birthday falls in May, was first heard at the Proms in 1997, with the UK concert premiere of his orchestral work *Liquid Marble*. Written in 2002, *Exquisite Corpse* was inspired by an old parlour game adopted as a method of random collaboration by the Surrealists. A form of consequences, in which each player adds a word or phrase to a poem without seeing the previous contributions, it took its name from one early product of this process, the classic Surrealist sentence *Le cadavre exquis boira le vin nouveau* (The exquisite corpse will drink the young wine). While Hillborg's work isn't actually collaborative, it was written as if a number of composers had come together to create it in the manner of a *cadavre exquis*. 'I tried consciously to combine disparate material from my own pieces as well as those of other composers. For example, there's a chord from *Petrushka*, a style quotation from Ligeti, a (hidden) quotation from Sibelius.' The result is complex and compelling, reflecting Hillborg's ear for multi-hued sonority, as well as his early career in rock music and as a student of such disparate figures as Brian Ferneyhough and Morton Feldman.

PROM 63

Alun Hoddinott (b. 1929)

Euphonium Concerto
London premiere

It's almost half a century since Alun Hoddinott's music was first heard at the Proms, when Gervase de Peyer performed the Clarinet Concerto, the work that launched Hoddinott's international career. This year the doyen of Welsh music celebrates his 75th birthday with a bulging commission book, including a trombone concerto, a song-cycle for baritone, horn and strings celebrating the scenery around the Gower peninsula near Swansea where Hoddinott now lives, a brass quintet, and a concerto grosso for brass band.

The Euphonium Concerto was composed for the BBC Young Musician finalist David Childs, who gave its premiere with the young chamber ensemble Sinfonia Cymru at Llandaff Cathedral in 2002. Hoddinott had been impressed by Childs's crusade to get the euphonium accepted as a serious orchestral instrument. Struck by the virtuosity that can be achieved by players brought up in the brass band tradition, Hoddinott has since followed up the Concerto with a Euphonium Sonata, also written for Childs and premiered by him last year.

PCM 8

Simon Holt (b. 1958)

The Coroner's Report
BBC commission: world premiere

Bolton-born Simon Holt recently enjoyed great success with his mystery opera *Who Put Bella in the Wych Elm?*, composed for last summer's Aldeburgh and Almeida festivals. His music was last heard at the Proms in 2002, when Jean Rigby and the Birmingham Contemporary Music Group performed his Lorca-inspired *Canciones*. But his association with the Proms dates back to 1987, when the orchestral *Syrensong* was premiered by the BBC Symphony Orchestra; five years later Nobuko Imai was the soloist with the BBC Philharmonic in the viola concerto *walking with the river's roar*. More recent BBC commissions include *eco-pavan*, composed for a 40th-birthday retrospective at the Huddersfield Festival, and *Two Movements*, written for the Belcea Quartet (BBC New Generation Artists at the time).

The Coroner's Report, the new work to be premiered by Nicholas Daniel and the Britten Sinfonia in this year's Proms Chamber Music series, is a follow-up to *Bella*, offering new bits of evidence that may cast fresh light on the unsolved murder that inspired the opera.

PROM 44

Kaija Saariaho (b. 1952)

Orion
UK premiere

Since studying at IRCAM in Paris and falling under the influence of the 'spectralist' composers Gérard Grisey and Tristan Murail in the early 1980s, the Finnish composer Kaija Saariaho has focused on large-scale soundscapes, swirling masses of sound relying more on rich tonal colours and textures than fleeting snatches of melody or definite rhythm. She has often achieved her unique acoustic landscapes through electronic manipulation of sounds, drawing inspiration from visual or poetic ideas. Her music was last heard at the Proms in 1995, when Gidon Kremer gave the world premiere of her violin concerto *Graal Théâtre*, a BBC co-commission. Her first opera, *L'amour de loin*, was premiered in 2000 at the Salzburg Festival and given a London performance the following year by the BBC Symphony Orchestra. Subsequent works have included the flute concerto *Aile du songe*, and *Nymphea Reflections* for string orchestra; a second opera is due to open at the Paris Opéra in 2006.

Orion was premiered last year by the Cleveland Orchestra under Franz Welser-Möst. Cast in three movements, it depicts Orion as constellation, mythical hunter and demigod, tracing his passage across the sky, painting eerie, icy sounds on a glacial, serenely effective canvas.

PROM 24

Esa-Pekka Salonen (b. 1958)
Laughing Unlearnt
London premiere

Fresh from presiding over the opening of the new Walt Disney Hall in Los Angeles, Esa-Pekka Salonen's double life as both composer and conductor shows no sign of slowing down. Following the UK premieres at the Proms of his *Insomnia* last season and *Foreign Bodies* in 2001,

his solo violin work *Laughing Unlearnt* will be given its London premiere this season by Cho-Liang Lin, who gave the premiere at the La Jolla Festival in California in 2002. Taking its title (*Lachen verlernt* in the original German) from Schoenberg's expressionist cabaret *Pierrot lunaire*, *Laughing Unlearnt* continues the darker strand in Salonen's usually sunny music that began with *Insomnia*. Salonen felt that the work might be suited to Lin's cheerful personality, which he suspects may have its darker side. The work is a set of variations over a

set of chords that are never heard – Bach's monumental *Chaconne* seems to be the clearest influence. But the laughter is regained at the end, a sweet coda to this allusive, virtuosic work.

PROM 63

Joby Talbot (b. 1971)
Sneaker Wave
BBC commission: world premiere

Joby Talbot's music was first heard at the Proms in 2002 – he was one of the contributors to the modern-day *Triumphs of Oriana*, performed by the King's Singers in a special Late Night Prom. Although he is probably best known for his work with The Divine Comedy and his music for television (*The League of Gentlemen*, BBC Young Musician and Comic Relief's *Robbie the Reindeer*), his music is increasingly being performed by classical

groups such as the London Sinfonietta and the BBC Symphony and Philharmonic orchestras. He is currently working on a piece for the guitarist Tom Kerstens, and a large-scale choral work about the pilgrimage to Santiago de Compostela.

Watching the sea during a recent visit to California, Talbot witnessed the phenomenon of the 'sneaker wave' – a wave that catches up with, or sneaks up on, a smaller one in front, subsuming its energy, growing and breaking, and chasing you up the beach. He was composing his BBC commission at the time, and had the idea of putting a sneaker wave into it. 'You'll know it when it comes,' he promises.

PROM 48

Mark-Anthony Turnage (b. 1960)
Calmo
BBC commission: world premiere

Since ending his stint as the BBC Symphony Orchestra's Associate Composer with a premiere-rich 'Composer Weekend' in January 2003, there has been no let-up in Mark-Anthony Turnage's prolific productivity. Fittingly, *No Let Up* is the title of one of his recent works,

premiered in Chicago in February; other premieres this year include *Crying Out Loud*, introduced in Frankfurt in March, and the first UK performance of the viola concerto *On Opened Ground*, given by the BBC SO at the Barbican the same month.

The BBC Symphony Chorus – for whose 75th anniversary *The Game Is Over* was written and first performed at the January Weekend – are also the recipients of *Calmo*, a short new work for choir with bells.

See also 'East/West', pages 4–12, for new works by Tan Dun, Zhou Long and Bright Sheng; see 'Season Highlights', page 65, for John Tavener's 'The Veil of the Temple'; see Prom 59 for Carl Vine's 'Celebrare celeberrime'

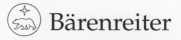

BBC Symphony Chorus 75

75th Anniversary Season

Director Stephen Jackson

75th Anniversary Season

The BBC Symphony Chorus has been celebrating its 75th anniversary with a season of remarkable performances including the world premiere of *Variations I for Stephen Montague* by John Cage, Berlioz's *L'enfance du Christ* in Westminster Cathedral and concerts at the Barbican.

The 75th anniversary celebrations draw to a close during the 2004 BBC Proms season as the BBC Symphony Chorus takes part in the First and Last Nights and gives its own Late Night Prom with music including newly-commissioned works by Judith Bingham and Mark-Anthony Turnage.

2004–05 Season Highlights

As usual, the BBC Symphony Chorus will be performing at the Barbican during the BBC Symphony Orchestra's 2004–05 Barbican season. Highlights include:

Mahler Symphony No 2, conducted by Jukka-Pekka Saraste
Mozart *Requiem*, conducted by Jiří Bělohlávek
John Adams *Harmonium*, conducted by the composer
James MacMillan *Quickening*, in the BBC SO's 2005 January Composer Weekend.

Would you like to join us?

The BBC Symphony Chorus is always interested in hearing from potential new members. If you would enjoy making music at the highest level with great conductors and orchestras, then this is the choir for you.

To find out more, contact Graham Wood, Chorus Administrator, or visit our website.

BBC Maida Vale Studios
Delaware Road
London W9 2LG
Tel: 020 7765 4715
Fax: 020 7286 3251
e-mail: graham.wood@bbc.co.uk

www.bbc.co.uk/orchestras/so/chorus

BBC RADIO 3

90-93 FM

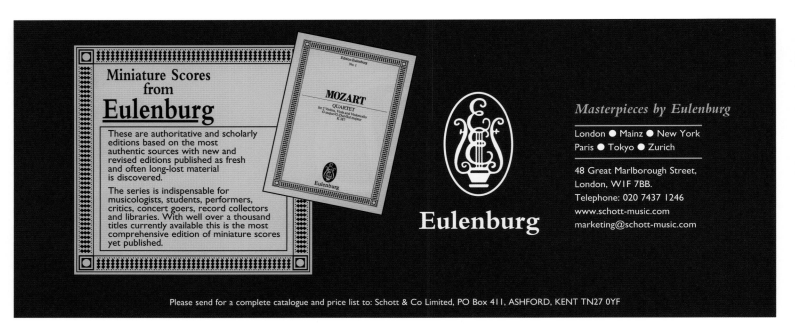

DIAGHILEV: The dancing years

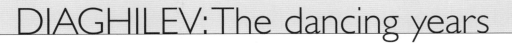

On the 75th anniversary of Diaghilev's death, **Christopher Cook** celebrates the lasting legacy of the great impresario

'Étonne-moi,' he would tell his collaborators. And they certainly astonished him and us. They still do. The very name Diaghilev has become synonymous with cultural patronage on an imperial scale and, more than that, patronage with unequalled taste and a rare appetite for the new. Stravinsky, Ravel, Debussy, Prokofiev, Satie and Poulenc all wrote for his dancers. Benois, Bakst, Larionov, Goncharova, Picasso, Matisse, Derain and Braque all designed for him. Diaghilev created an art form in which, for the very first time, dance and design and music met as equals.

Yet Sergey Pavlovich Diaghilev never made anything himself. He was an enabler of other people's gifts and he turned them into other people's tastes. When the Ballets Russes first conquered the West in the early 1900s, smart Parisians redesigned their salons in Bakst's thrilling primitive colours from the East and bought new wardrobes for their wives.

It was a search for novelty that led Diaghilev to his greatest composer, Igor Stravinsky, who'd scarcely cut his musical teeth when he was asked to write *The Firebird* in 1910. A year later came *Petrushka* and then the notorious *Rite of Spring*. A scandal, with fisticuffs in the stalls. Diaghilev's comment afterwards? 'Just what I wanted.' It was good for art and good for business.

In his first scores for Diaghilev Stravinsky helped to move classical dance in an entirely new direction. This was music that demanded a new kind of choreography. Mikhail Fokine laid the foundations of the Diaghilev style and, when he was dismissed, Nijinsky took his place. He had already shocked stuffy Paris with his first dance, to Debussy's *Prélude à L'après-midi d'un faune*. It wasn't the stark gestures of the dancers or the influence of Greek sculpture that upset the audience, but the faun making very obvious love to a nymph's scarf.

Nijinsky was the first of Diaghilev's favourites and the great impresario's preference for male lovers who were also dancers finally gave the male classical dancer more than a supporting role. After Nijinsky came Massine and Lifar. But while Nijinsky is still remembered as the most luminous of Diaghilev's boys, it was his sister Bronislava who created the more enduring choreography, in her two 1920s masterpieces, *Renard* and *Les noces*, to scores by Stravinsky. And, with singers in the pit as well as musicians, both continued to break the mould of what classical dance was supposed to be.

As a young man, Diaghilev wrote to his stepmother, 'I am first a great charlatan, but with brio; secondly a great *charmeur*; thirdly, I have any amount of cheek; fourthly, I am a man with a great quantity of logic, but very few principles; fifthly, I think I have no real gifts. All the same, I have just found my true vocation – being a Maecenas. I have all that is necessary, save the money – *mais ça viendra*.' Luckily it did, and we're all the richer for it.

LEFT
Inside the harem: set design by Léon Bakst for Fokine's oriental ballet *Schéhérazade*, premiered by the Diaghilev company in Paris in 1910

ABOVE
Vaslav Nijinsky as Petrushka in the 1911 Paris premiere of Stravinsky's second Diaghilev commission

TOP RIGHT
Diaghilev with his old nurse: portrait by Bakst, c1905

BOTTOM RIGHT
A Royal Ballet revival of *Les noces*, the last Stravinsky ballet to be premiered by Diaghilev

PROM 8	**STRAVINSKY: The Firebird** Thursday 22 July, 7.30pm
PROM 11	**STRAVINSKY: Petrushka** Saturday 24 July, 7.30pm
PROM 42	**STRAVINSKY: The Rite of Spring** Monday 16 August, 7.30pm
PROM 60	**DEBUSSY: Prélude à L'après-midi d'un faune** Monday 30 August, 7.30pm
PROM 65	**STRAVINSKY: Les noces** Friday 3 September, 10.00pm
PROM 71	**STRAVINSKY: Renard** Wednesday 8 September, 10.00pm

MESSIAEN: En route to Paradise

Olivier Messiaen's music is among the most spiritually engaged of our time. It has its eastern echoes but, explains **Malcolm Hayes**, its roots lie in a more specifically European, Catholic and even medieval mode of thinking

'I am a composer of the Middle Ages.' Messiaen's description of himself might at first seem remote from his stature as one of the 20th century's front-rank musicians. But throughout his life he continued, with a self-knowledge as complete as it was clear-minded, to draw on the sources of inspiration he discovered very early – sources not so much modern as timeless.

His unwavering Catholic faith arrived in childhood, as did his love of nature and birdsong. The mountains around Grenoble, where he grew up, were always where he preferred to compose. A vocal score of Debussy's opera *Pelléas et Mélisande*, a 10th birthday present, was a decisive revelation. So was a childhood visit to Paris's Sainte-Chapelle. (Some 70 years later Messiaen said: 'Stained glass is one of the most wonderful creations of man. You are overwhelmed. And I think this is the beginning of Paradise.') Technical discoveries followed at the Paris Conservatoire: Indian rhythmic cycles (found in inaccurate transcriptions in an encyclopedia) and 'modes of limited transposition' – exotic scales as a basis for exotic harmony.

Messiaen's mature style crystallised so early that the iridescent sound-world of *Poèmes pour Mi* (1936–7) is already as individual as its inspiration: Mi was the nickname of Messiaen's first wife, and his words and music celebrate the sacrament of marriage, between two people as between Christ and the Church. The years that followed saw a musical stance that became much more public and rhetorical, culminating in the vast and spectacular *Turangalîla Symphony* (1946–8). Yet here too, in a non-Christian context, the medieval credentials of Messiaen's art are unmistakable: the intersection of immense and intricate architectural scale – dedicated (in this case indirectly) to the glory of God – with the sensuous shock of colour.

In the decade after *Turangalîla*, Messiaen built entire works out of meticulous transcriptions of birdsong: for him, each bird was a self-contained musical symbol, singing of the resurrected soul's joy. *Le merle noir* (1951), written as a test piece for flautists at the Paris Conservatoire, is as characteristic of its composer as are much larger creations. His later works then became increasingly large, presenting each facet of divine contemplation in musical images of burgeoning range and variety. *Des canyons aux étoiles …* (1971–4) was inspired by the red sandstone spires of Bryce Canyon in Utah. Messiaen's last major statement was *Éclairs sur l'Au-delà …* (1988–92), a vision of a Paradise to be encountered quite soon now. Many years earlier he had been asked if he would compose a *Requiem*. 'Death?' he responded. 'That exists. But I myself emphasise the Resurrection.'

BELOW
A glimpse of Paradise?
Olivier Messiaen against the stained glass windows of the Sainte-Chapelle, Paris

IVES: The All-American Dreamer

ABOVE
Charles Ives, a composer of 'fine strong music' inspired by the landscape, history and hymns of his native New England (right)

Half a century after Charles Ives's death, **Calum MacDonald** celebrates the Connecticut-born band-leader's son turned insurance salesman who grew up to make a million on Liberty Street, married a girl called Harmony and became America's most lastingly original composer

In some ways Charles Ives's life typified the American capitalist dream. From a small-town boyhood, son of the town band-leader, he rose to become a millionaire insurance executive, an innovator in his business just as in his music. In reality he was a highly unusual man, in advance of his age. Even in the idyllic New England boyhood he loved to recall, he felt out of place. We feel this dichotomy in the music: Ives is the master of the big, bad noise curtailed by a sigh or a catch of the breath. He seems to have been extremely shy and sensitive, preternaturally aware of the smallest sounds around him. Yet no composer was bolder in transcribing and transforming the 'Sound of Life' in all its raucous, polyrhythmic dissonance.

Ives's outer, robust, downright Yankee persona was constructed partly by force of will. But it was through music that he retained his boyhood identity: the hymns of the church and the revival meetings, the barn dances, the marches and popular songs. He carried them with him into manhood, and into his music. Ives's creative vision – nourished by US history, its authors and thinkers, but above all its music – remembers the past. It remembers, in the title of one of his many, astonishing songs, 'The Things Our

Fathers Loved (And The Greatest of Those Was Liberty)'. Paradoxically, the completeness and intensity of the remembering put him ahead of practically every other musician of his time. The liberties he took in flouting the genteel musical conventions were rooted in his concern for the basic principles of American democracy, and his sharp awareness of the forces which, in his time as in ours, keep those principles under permanent threat.

Few of his works were performed, far less understood, when he wrote them; recognition only started to come in the 1930s, after he'd written his last music, and it was not until long after his death, in 1954, that he was acknowledged as the first and greatest original among American composers.

The Fourth Symphony and the 'Concord' Sonata are two of his most inspired works, on the largest and the most intimate instrumental scale: interrelated, and each drawing on many earlier musical projects to force them into a teeming unity. Whitman-like, they 'contain multitudes'. They unite the extremes of Ives's musical personality, from the homely and hymnic to the abrasively exploratory, celebrating life's diversity – comedy, tragedy, the Transcendental ideals of the 19th-century American philosophers and novelists, Thoreau's worship of nature, the religious impulse that underlies all things. 'Fine strong music' was Ives's ideal, and here he unquestionably achieved it.

PROM 11 **IVES: Symphony No. 4**
Saturday 24 July, 7.30pm

PROM 49 **IVES: Songs (arr. Adams)**
Sunday 22 August, 6.30pm

PCM 7 **IVES: 'Concord' Sonata**
Monday 30 August, 1.00pm

BRITTEN: War Requiem

David Matthews describes how Benjamin Britten borrowed the words of the First World War poet Wilfred Owen to help build a personal memorial to pacifism upon the bombed-out ruins of Coventry's medieval cathedral

'My subject is War, and the pity of War. The Poetry is in the pity … All a poet can do today is warn.'

Wilfred Owen's words stand at the head of the score of Benjamin Britten's *War Requiem*, his great artistic statement of pacifism. Britten was a pacifist throughout his life. At school he had refused to join the Officers' Training Corps, and his anti-war attitudes were stimulated by long conversations with his composition teacher Frank Bridge about the First World War. In the 1930s he was actively engaged with the Peace Pledge Union and, on returning to England from the USA during the Second World War, he and his partner, the tenor Peter Pears, declared themselves conscientious objectors. In his statement to the tribunal (from which they both succeeded in obtaining exemption from war service), Britten declared: 'The whole of my life has been devoted to acts of creation … and I cannot take part in acts of destruction.'

The opportunity to express his deepest feelings about war came in 1958 when Britten was asked to compose a large-scale work for the consecration of the new Coventry Cathedral, built on the ruins of the medieval cathedral which had been almost entirely destroyed by bombs in 1940. Britten came up with a radically innovative scheme. He interspersed the movements of the Latin Mass for the Dead, set for soprano, chorus and large orchestra, with poems by Owen – the most searingly subversive of the First World War poets – set for tenor and baritone soloists, with chamber orchestra, that subjectify and sometimes implicitly criticise the Requiem texts. So, for example, the liturgical last trump in the *Dies irae* is followed by Owen's poem 'Bugles sang, saddening the evening air'; and, most tellingly, the confident claim of the *Offertorium*, 'quam olim Abrahae promisisti, et semini eius' ('which you once promised to Abraham, and his seed'), is undermined by Owen's devastating reinterpretation of the Abraham and Isaac story, ending with 'the old man would not so, but slew his son, – And half the seed of Europe, one by one', lines that Britten repeats over and over again while the boys' chorus impotently sing the words of the liturgy.

At the work's first performance in May 1963, at which Britten had hoped to have English, German and Russian soloists (but the Soviets would not allow Galina Vishnevskaya to stand beside Dietrich Fischer-Dieskau), the final hushed 'Amen' was followed by a long, stunned silence. Almost everyone in the audience realised that they had witnessed the birth of that rare phenomenon, a modern classic. More than 40 years later, at a time when, far from retreating, war rages feverishly around the world, the *War Requiem*'s warning message is still urgently relevant.

TOP
Benjamin Britten: composer, pacifist and conscientious objector

ABOVE
'All a poet can do today is warn': Wilfred Owen, who was killed on 4 November 1918, just a week before the Armistice

BOTTOM LEFT
Mourning a fallen comrade, August 1917

BRITTEN: War Requiem
Sunday 1 August, 6.30pm

PROM 22

TAVENER: The Veil of the Temple

As Sir John Tavener's cosmic journey comes to the Proms in a new compact version to mark his 60th birthday, **Richard Morrison** recalls how its all-night premiere converted at least one doubting Thomas

ABOVE
The Choir of the Temple Church, London, where Tavener's all-night vigil was first performed last year

TOP RIGHT
Sir John Tavener

It cost almost half a million pounds to commission and rehearse. It ran to 850 pages of full score and incorporated chants, prayers and psalms from all the world's major religions, with a few of the more esoteric ones tossed in for good measure. And its premiere was a night that nobody present will forget.

When a solo soprano, veiled from head to foot like some ghostly apparition, floated her first ethereal notes through the 13th-century Temple Church, off Fleet Street, it was dusk on a midsummer evening. By the time that 150 singers, a brass band, organ, gong, Tibetan horn and temple bells had thundered out a wild and jubilant rendition of the great Hindu 'Upanishad Hymn' and led the entire audience out of the church in a kind of metaphysical conga-dance, dawn had broken over London.

That was how Sir John Tavener's *The Veil of the Temple* was revealed to an astonished musical world last June. Running for seven hours, it is probably the longest vocal work ever composed, far outstripping a mere trifle such as Wagner's *The Mastersingers*.

But it wasn't really the length of this 'journey to the centre of the Cosmos' that mesmerised those who heard it. It was the gradual, but finally overwhelming, piling-up not only of musical and theological material (the piece comprises eight liturgical cycles presenting the same modes and refrains with increasing richness, complexity and power) but also of something far less tangible. Something that can only be described as spiritual ecstasy.

As the hours ticked by, and the Greek incense wafted more thickly, and more and more candles were lit, and the recurring

the piece developed a primordial force that was at first hypnotic, then almost terrifying in its fervour. It climaxed with eight ear-splitting whacks on the tam-tam, accompanied by blasts of Tibetan horn and organ. That was the Last Trump. Then the 'veil of the temple' itself – the final division between earthly and heavenly things – was metaphorically torn away, signifying that humanity's petty distinctions were dissolved, and all creation had become as one with its creator.

The Veil is surely Tavener's masterpiece. It is the culmination of, and perhaps also the justification for, all those decades' worth of famously spun-out drones, vaguely Eastern-sounding incantations and endless repetitions. Now it is being taken up by the Proms, in honour of the great mystic's 60th birthday. In the vast spaces of the Royal Albert Hall, and condensed to a 'mere' 160 minutes, its impact will inevitably change. But this lifelong 'Tavnostic' will certainly be there, in the hope of experiencing its unique power once again.

PROM 23

TAVENER: The Veil of the Temple
Sunday 1 August, 9.00pm

BACH: Mass in B minor

At once a compendium of his compositional skills and a credo of his personal faith, Bach's mighty Latin Mass was also, **Lindsay Kemp** suggests, intended to stake his place in history

Romantic notions die hard. We still like to think of great artists as having overcome hardship, lived unrecognised and been original, even ahead of their time. For the 19th-century rediscoverers of Bach, the Leipzig Cantor seemed just such a figure, obscurely and selflessly turning out church cantatas every week out of pure devotion to God, with never a thought of earthly fame or fortune. Scholarship has since modified this view: we know now that Bach worked very much in the real world; that his position as music director at St Thomas's Church in Leipzig was a highly respected one; and that, far from creating masterpieces in isolation, he surpassed the achievements of those who had gone before him by studying and respecting them.

There is, however, a kernel of truth in the romantic view, and nowhere is it better illustrated than in the great panels of the B minor Mass. For Bach, it seems, was much exercised about the idea of posterity. How else can we explain this giant work, too long to be used in any church service and not heard in full until over 100 years after the composer's death? Bach had begun it in 1733, when he set the first two sections, the Kyrie and Gloria, but it was not until the last years of his life, over a decade later, that he completed it by adding the Credo, Sanctus and Agnus Dei. What was he thinking of?

One answer seems plausible. That Bach had a sense of his place in history is shown by the detailed family tree that he drew up around 1735, but in the 1740s he became increasingly preoccupied with the preparation of 'theoretical' cycles of works wh_____ principal ___ __ __ ___ to __plor_ d_li_its of

compositional possibility – limits that, as he well knew, only he could reach. *The Art of Fugue* and the *Musical Offering*, both dating from this time, are exhaustive treatments of fugal and canonic writing respectively. Seen in this context, Bach's B minor Mass – not newly composed but skilfully recycling music from his cantatas, and running a gamut of contemporary vocal styles from old-fashioned choral counterpoint to decoratively up-to-date solo-writing – looks like a similar statement of his mastery of sacred vocal music.

And yes, faith does come into it. By rescuing some of the best of his earlier music from its ephemeral origins in the weekly Lutheran liturgy and harnessing it instead to the timeless ritual of the Latin Mass, Bach produced a universal artwork that stands testament to his Christian belief as well as to his supreme creative skill. In this work, perhaps more than in any other, Bach is telling us who he really is. This great, impractical masterpiece of the Baroque has something for the romantic in us after all.

WAGNER: Das Rheingold

ABOVE
Richard Wagner:
musical revolutionary

TOP RIGHT & BELOW
The three Rhinemaidens
in *The Ring*'s 1876 Bayreuth
premiere and, *below*, the
original costume designs for
Alberich, Wotan and Fafner

This year sees the start of the first-ever Proms *Ring* cycle, spread over four years and shared between different teams of performers. As the revolutionary nature of Wagner's massive score is highlighted by a period-instrument performance of its opening part, **Mike Ashman** charts the work's epic genesis

Richard Wagner's *Ring* is one of the largest works in Western music, lasting over 15 hours (excluding intervals). The story of its creation is a saga in itself. In 1848 – financial problems aside – Wagner looked to have it made. Not only was he increasingly successful as both composer and conductor, his life's work seemed planned out ahead: *The Flying Dutchman*, *Tannhäuser* and *Lohengrin* were all written, *Mastersingers* and *Parsifal* sketched or previewed, and an opera on the popular German hero Siegfried waiting to be begun. And the whole time Wagner was reading voraciously, supplementing his beloved Shakespeare, Aeschylus and Sophocles with a special study of the medieval Volsung and Nibelung stories in both their Norse and German versions.

Then came revolution, in which Wagner played his part. Fleeing abroad to avoid arrest, he virtually abandoned composition for the next five years, devoting himself instead to writing large-scale theoretical tracts about the nature and purpose of contemporary opera and the manner (and places) in which it should be performed.

By 1853 *Siegfrieds Tod* (Siegfried's Death), the three-act 'heroic grand opera' he had begun back in Dresden, had metamorphosed into a four-part cycle of music dramas, *Der Ring des Nibelungen* (The Ring of the Nibelung), to be performed over four days and encompassing no less than 'the beginning and end of the world'. It was to be another 23 years before it was first performed complete.

All the events of Wagner's recent life, both intellectual and political, were combined in the new work. It operated simultaneously on several levels – 'good story', political tract, philosophical commentary. As for the music, it had been purged of exhibitionistic vocal effects, while the orchestra was to play a more active role in the drama, providing complex emotional and geographical backdrops to the working-out of the Nibelung's curse.

For the opening scene of *Das Rheingold* (The Rhine Gold), the start of the entire cycle, Wagner posits a pre-history for the all-powerful ring not found in any ancient saga. It enabled him to place at the centre of his drama a psychological crisis: power over others can only be attained by giving up the most vital human emotion – love. We see the successive owners of the ring – Nibelung dwarf Alberich, chief god Wotan, giant worker Fafner – corrupted by the talisman into exploitation and murder, while Wagner's music carries us successively from the watery depths of the Rhine to airy mountain heights, down into the mines of Nibelheim and finally across a rainbow-bridge to the gods' new home, Valhalla.

As recent concert cycles of the *Ring* have shown, an oratorio-style approach permits greater concentration on Wagner's orchestral mastery. This season's Proms performance of *Das Rheingold* by Sir Simon Rattle and the Orchestra of the Age of Enlightenment – the first time a Wagner opera has been played on original instruments in modern times – promises new revelations, especially in the problematic balance between strings and brass. What other performers will bring to each of *The Ring*'s subsequent three parts, we'll all just have to wait and see.

PROM 45 | WAGNER: Das Rheingold
Thursday 19 August, 7.00pm

HUMPERDINCK: Hansel and Gretel

By mixing Wagnerian methods and folk melodies, Engelbert Humperdinck created a unique recipe for giving a Grimm tale a happy ending. As the Proms mark the composer's 150th anniversary with a performance of his most popular opera, **Michael Tanner** relishes the gilt on the gingerbread

Hansel and Gretel was the first opera to be broadcast complete in the UK, in 1923, and the first to be broadcast 'live from the Met' in the USA, on Christmas Day 1931. Since it was premiered under Richard Strauss in Weimar in 1893 it has never lost its popularity, either with audiences or performers. Yet Humperdinck, friend and disciple of Wagner and musical tutor to his son Siegfried, never repeated its success, and of his other works only *Königskinder*, another fairy-tale opera, retains a marginal place in the repertory.

Hansel began when Humperdinck's sister asked him to set to music some nursery rhymes she had written, and other members of the family subsequently joined in, making a play out of the Grimms' fairy tale. Humperdinck began to develop operatic ambitions, and his fiancée encouraged him, unsure of himself as he was. It was produced in 50 theatres in Germany within a year of its premiere, and even Cosima Wagner directed it.

The sheer idea of combining folk melodies with Wagner's compositional techniques sounds paradoxical, at least. Yet that is what the composer achieved. The glorious textures of the overture, beginning with the hushed beauty of the Children's Prayer, heard first on four horns, then with the full orchestra, gathering momentum and leading to a diversity of melodies, assure us that we are in for a happy evening, whatever troubles we and the children may encounter on the way.

There are some contemporary critics who talk of *Hansel* as being 'profoundly disturbing'. That is absurd. No opera with so melting an opening could be other than a rosy picture of childhood. Of course Hansel and Gretel are poor, and terribly hungry when the curtain rises. When Mother enters and spills the milk, it's a terrible moment. But, whereas in Grimm she plans to lose the children, in Humperdinck she is full of remorse for letting them go out alone. The wood is frightening, the Witch both funny and alarming. Yet the music is almost always reassuring, with its great tendrils of warm tunes burgeoning and surrounding the children, as a kind of protective cloak. The Witch is easily disposed of, with one shove pushed into her own oven. Naturally the idea of children being roasted can have resonances now that it lacked in 1893, but the Witch's plan was to eat them, which hardly fits in with the Holocaust.

At the end there is a sly parody of Wagner, with all the children who had previously been turned to gingerbread being 'redeemed'. Perhaps no work is so derivative and yet so perfect. Of all Wagner's followers, Humperdinck was the only one to benefit unequivocally from his Master's voice, so that his music sounds as fresh now as it did 111 years ago.

ABOVE
The Wicked Witch: cut-out figure from a 19th-century German toy-theatre sheet

BELOW
Engelbert Humperdinck

PROM 46
HUMPERDINCK: Hansel and Gretel
Friday 20 August, 7.00pm

RAKHMANINOV: The Miserly Knight

ABOVE
Sergey Rakhmaninov

BELOW
Fyodor Chaliapin, the great
Russian bass for whom
Rakhmaninov wrote *The
Miserly Knight*, though he
never sang it on stage:
portrait by Valentin Serov

Gerard McBurney reveals the Wagnerian roots of Rakhmaninov's bleak study of obsessive greed, being brought to the Proms by Glyndebourne as the first half of an appropriately money-driven double-bill

While Rakhmaninov's symphonies and concertos are staples of the Romantic repertoire, his three operas are much less well known and even more rarely staged. All are in one act. The first, *Aleko* (based on Pushkin's poem *The Gypsies*), is but a student work, though it won its 19-year-old composer the Great Gold Medal of the Moscow Conservatory, was given a prestige premiere at the Bolshoy and was much admired by Tchaikovsky. The other two, *The Miserly Knight* (another Pushkin setting) and *Francesca da Rimini* (after the familiar story in Dante's *Inferno*), were written in tandem some 15 years later, and premiered as a double-bill, with the composer himself conducting, at the Bolshoy in 1906.

Both were written as vehicles for the great dramatic bass Fyodor Chaliapin, with whom Rakhmaninov had become friendly during his two seasons as conductor of the Moscow Private Russian Opera. In the event, Chaliapin never sang either work on stage. He did, however, regularly include the long central monologue from *The Miserly Knight* in his concerts. No wonder. In its rich mix of Gothic grandeur, grand guignol, perverse passion and even an element of grotesque parody, the great soliloquy for the greedy Old Baron, the 'miserly knight' who spends his nights gloating, with almost sexual frenzy, over his hidden hoard of gold, is a gift to any singing actor.

If the influence of Tchaikovsky is clear from the work's very first bars, as well as in its melodramatically 'fateful' ending, the crucial influence is, perhaps surprisingly, that of Wagner. From him Rakhmaninov learnt how to create a seamless symphonic flow by building his music not out of big, romantic

tunes (the sort of thing we usually associate with Rakhmaninov) but out of small, fragmentary *leitmotifs* that represent ideas like greed and despair and so tell us exactly what is going on inside the characters' heads. Rakhmaninov, who had made the pilgrimage to Bayreuth on his honeymoon in 1902, chose to set Pushkin's play precisely because it has so many parallels with Wagner's *Ring*, which also explores the destructive effects of gold on human relationships. The Old Baron, hoarding his riches, is uncannily like Wagner's giant Fafner, guarding his gold in dragon form, while the tenorial dispute between the Baron's grasping son Albert and Salomon, the money-lender, echoes the bickering between Wagner's young hero Siegfried and his wheedling foster-father, the dwarf Mime (and is equally open to charges of anti-Semitism). But unlike *The Ring* – or Puccini's *Gianni Schicchi*, the second half of Glyndebourne's double-bill *(see overleaf)* – Rakhmaninov's devastatingly bleak ending holds out no hope of final redemption.

PROM 55

RAKHMANINOV: The Miserly Knight
Thursday 26 August, 7.30pm

PUCCINI: Gianni Schicchi

Doomed by Dante to eternal damnation in the Eighth Circle of Hell, Gianni Schicchi, the deathbed swindler, was brought back to operatic life as the conman hero of Puccini's only comedy. **Nicholas Payne** introduces the second half of Glyndebourne's money-driven double-bill

Successful comedies are more elusive than tragedies in opera. Only late in life did Verdi achieve his with *Falstaff*. Puccini, perhaps conscious of the older composer's legacy, only tried once but, to his surprise, *Gianni Schicchi* proved easier to write than the tear-inducing dramas at which he was so expert.

He originally conceived it as the third panel of a triptych of one-acters, premiered in New York in 1918. *Il tabarro* (The Cloak) is a slice of contemporary low-life realism set on a barge on the River Seine. *Suor Angelica* breathes elevated religious sentiment, teetering on the brink of sentimentality, in a 17th-century convent. *Gianni Schicchi* is placed precisely in Florence in 1299, and is the 'satyr play' that unwinds and releases the tragic tensions.

The story is no more than an anecdote, culled from a passing reference to a real-life Florentine peasant in Dante's *Inferno*. Dante, a noble Florentine, condemns the upstart Schicchi to eternal torment for his crime of altering the will of Buoso Donati by impersonating the dead man. Puccini, a professional musician from backwoods Lucca, is more sympathetic to his conman hero. Merciless in depicting the greedy relations of the departed with *commedia dell'arte*

caricature, he humanises the sly and cunning Schicchi with music that energises the score with laughter.

Schicchi does not appear until about a third of the way into the opera, but his spirit precedes him. The score opens with a great burst of orchestral laughter, which keeps bubbling up again to punctuate the hypocritically repetitious mourning of Buoso's bereaved family. Schicchi's advocate and ally is the tenor nephew Rinuccio, who loves his daughter Lauretta and admires the resourcefulness of her father. It is Lauretta's lilting plea 'O mio babbino caro' (O my beloved father) that melts Schicchi's heart just enough for him to consider helping the patricians he despises. The trick is that, by winning their connivance, he helps himself, in more ways than one.

The other great affirmative of this little opera is its depiction of Renaissance Florence, a city noted for its devious rogues but also for the brilliance of its citizens and its artists. The opera celebrates its contradictions. Schicchi's ruse having disposed of the venal relations, the future belongs to the young lovers Rinuccio and Lauretta, who reclaim Puccini's trademark lyricism, at first in snatches, finally in its full glory. 'We shall always stay here,' sings Rinuccio, remembering their first kiss in the golden city and how it seemed like Paradise. For Schicchi, it's Hell that beckons. But he asks us the audience, if we have been amused, to allow him extenuating circumstances. 'Could Buoso's money have finished up better than this?'

ABOVE
Giacomo Puccini

LEFT
Gianni Schicchi: costume design for the title-role at the 1918 New York Metropolitan premiere

PROM 55

PUCCINI: Gianni Schicchi
Thursday 26 August, 7.30pm

MONTEVERDI: Vespers of 1610

As Monteverdi's sacred masterpiece makes its first Proms appearance in the Royal Albert Hall, **Robert King** finds himself as amazed by the score's startling modernity as he was when he first worked on it 25 years ago

'I heard the best musicke that ever I did in all my life ... so good that I would willingly goe an hundred miles a foote at any time to heare the like ... so good, so delectable, so rare, so admirable, so superexcellent, that it did even ravish and stupifie all those strangers that never heard the like.'

The traveller Thomas Coryat, writing in 1611 after a visit to Venice, was transported to levels of hyperbole that even today's raciest columnists might find hard to surpass. He heard music that was unlike anything he had experienced before. But what was this new style that so excited him, and why was it so radical? Where had it come from?

The answers lie with a generation of remarkable Italian composers: at their head stands the astonishing figure of Claudio Monteverdi. Not without good reason has he been called 'the Grandfather of classical music'. He took the musical styles of the later 16th century, turned them around and spun them into radical, new directions. Whether writing brilliantly expressive madrigals, powerfully dramatic operas or colourful and highly imaginative sacred music, Monteverdi everywhere wrote in a direct, emotional style which still speaks with an immediacy and a modernity that never fail to amaze.

His *Vespro della Beata Vergine*, published in 1610, must surely be one of the most impressive job applications ever made. By 1608, buoyed by the success of his new opera *Orfeo*, he was outgrowing his position at the court in Mantua: he needed to

show his qualifications for a substantial church post. His solution was to publish a large volume comprising a Mass (written in conservative style, so as not to shock the Counter-Reformists) and a dazzling new collection of music for Vespers. Its opulence, modernity and invention constituted an ideal c.v. to submit to those great churches and court chapels where he hoped to find work. Whether as a direct result or not, in 1613 Monteverdi was invited to perform some of his sacred music at an audition in the famous Venetian basilica of San Marco. He was appointed Maestro di Cappella, remaining there for another 30 years.

More than 150 sacred compositions survive, written across a magnificently wide range of styles, but he did not restrict himself to church music alone. Great operas continued to flow, including *The Coronation of Poppea* and *The Return of Ulysses*. His influence on composers spread through France and Germany, lasting right through to the age of Bach.

I filled my 'gap year' before university, exactly 25 years ago, making a performing edition of Monteverdi's *Vespers*, and have regularly returned to the work, for it is one of the great cornerstones of classical music: magnificent and sonorous, sensuous, rhythmically thrilling, simultaneously backward- and forward-looking. Music that is rare, admirable and, indeed, superexcellent!

ABOVE RIGHT
Claudio Monteverdi: Renaissance modernist

BELOW
The interior of St Mark's, Venice, where Monteverdi was Maestro di Cappella for 30 years

BELOW RIGHT
The Piazza San Marco, c1730, by Canaletto

MONTEVERDI: Vespers of 1610
Tuesday 31 August, 7.30pm

PROM 61

71

CHARPENTIER: Sacred music

Marc-Antoine Charpentier gave Eurovision its theme tune and Les Arts Florissants its name. As the Parisian period ensemble visits the Proms to mark the 300th anniversary of his death (and the 25th anniversary of its debut), **Graham Sadler** profiles the man now widely recognised as the leading French composer of his day

During the past 30 years the musical reputation of Marc-Antoine Charpentier has undergone an astonishing transformation. As recently as 1973 J. R. Anthony's respected *French Baroque Music* could state, not unfairly, that Charpentier's music had 'barely survived the 18th century'. Since then, thanks partly to the pioneering work of ensembles like Les Arts Florissants, a whole generation of music-lovers has begun to discover the richness and variety in this composer's huge output. Today he is regarded as by far the finest French composer of the 17th century.

Not that Charpentier enjoyed universal acclaim in his own day. For conservative listeners, the very features that we so enjoy – bold dissonances, quirky harmonies, chromatic intervals – seemed harsh or unnatural. His style, which to us sounds unmistakably French, was regarded as too Italianate, corrupted by his youthful studies with Carissimi in Rome. Moreover, Charpentier was doubtless seen as a threat by the ambitious Lully, who may have had something to do with his young contemporary's failure to gain a major appointment at Louis XIV's court. Likewise, Charpentier had to wait until Lully's death before being allowed to compose for the Paris Opéra. And although his masterpiece *Médée* (1693) was praised by Brossard as 'the one opera, above all others, from which may be learnt the essentials of good composition', it was more generally received with uncomprehending indifference.

Little surprise, then, that Charpentier could reflect bitterly on his career, albeit in the context of a spoof memorial cantata, *Epitaphium Carpentarij*. Here his ghost makes the extraordinary confession that 'since those who scorned me were more numerous than those who praised me, music became a small honour and a heavy burden'.

Happily there were those who appreciated his extraordinary talent. The playwright Molière was an early champion. Another was the Duchess of Guise, for whom three of the works in this season's tercentenary Prom were written – the hauntingly elegiac *Messe pour les trépassés* (Mass for the Departed), its associated motet and the more dramatic *Dies irae*. She may even have commissioned the instrumental Mass also included in the programme, in which the composer uses exotic orchestration to evoke the colours of the organ.

Charpentier also held several prestigious church posts, notably at the Jesuit church of St Paul-St Louis, for which his *Te Deum* was composed. Thanks to Eurovision's use of the opening fanfare as its signature tune for the past 50 years, this has become one of Charpentier's best-known works. It forms an appropriately celebratory conclusion to this season's tercentenary tribute.

LEFT
Mademoiselle de Guise (1615–88), the duchess for whom Charpentier wrote his *Mass for the Departed*

ABOVE
The Jesuit church of St Paul-St Louis in Paris, where Charpentier was employed as *maître de musique* and for which he wrote his *Te Deum*

PROM 72
CHARPENTIER: Sacred music
Thursday 9 September, 7.30pm

BBC SINGERS

2004 concerts include appearances in Belfast, Cambridge, Cheltenham, Edinburgh, London, Lancaster, Manchester, Metz, Norwich, Preston & Tallinn

Chief Conductor
Stephen Cleobury

Principal Guest Conductor
Bob Chilcott

Associate Composer
Edward Cowie

'The BBC Singers yielded some thrilling results'
Independent 06/02/04
Review of Maxwell Davies concert

'The BBC Singers proved themselves as much a band of soloists as a sentient and sensitive ensemble'
Times 19/12/03
Review of Spitalfields Winter Festival concert

GERALD PLACE

For more information about forthcoming concerts, join the Friends of the BBC Singers

Tel 020 7765 1862   **Email** singers@bbc.co.uk   **www.bbc.co.uk/singers**

BBC RADIO 3 90-93FM

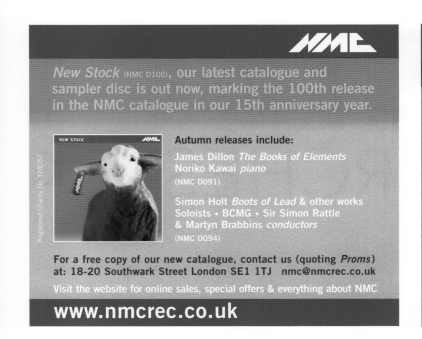

BBC Proms 2004

Three concerts, with **Maxwell Davies'** First Taverner Fantasia conducted by Martyn Brabbins, **Janáček's** The Eternal Gospel and **Mahler's** Seventh Symphony conducted by Ilan Volkov

2004/2005 Season includes

Bartók	Duke Bluebeard's Castle
Britten	War Requiem
Messiaen	Turangalila

BBC SCOTTISH SYMPHONY ORCHESTRA

Chief Conductor Ilan Volkov

www.bbc.co.uk/bbcsso

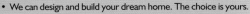

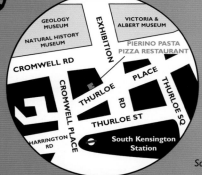

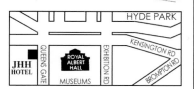

ARTISTS

PROMS

In the spotlight

Well over 200 guest artists appear at the Proms each year. Here, nine of this season's top soloists talk to **Claire Rogers** about the works they're performing in 2004

PCM 7

Pierre-Laurent Aimard plays
Ives 'Concord' Sonata

'We tend to think of Ives as a modern composer, but the 'Concord' Sonata was written almost a century ago. I first played it in 1974, and it's always had a great significance for me. Ives was a pioneer, with a level of independence and freedom in his writing that was incredible. This marvellous modernism makes him a kind of prophet, but there's also an incredible freshness – he produces the most astonishingly modern, strange, and sometimes even vulgar ideas, which almost sound as if they came from a child.

The 'Concord' Sonata is extremely challenging, not only because it includes difficult passages in terms of polyphony and virtuosity, but also because of its size. The meaning of the piece, its transcendentalism, is another challenge. So, as an interpreter, you have to deal with a lot of dimensions to bring out its real significance.'

Pierre-Laurent Aimard also plays Ravel's Piano Concerto in G major in Prom 8

PROM 58

Yuri Bashmet plays
Bartók Viola Concerto

'I have played the Bartók Viola Concerto many times and it's a piece which I love very much. In the history of the instrument I think it is the most important work ever written. Bartók was a pioneer, the first to write for the viola as a solo instrument on this kind of scale. Other works had already been written for it, of course, but mostly without any great depth or significance. But Bartók gave it such important musical information to convey, just as Brahms did for the violin in his concerto, after which the violin began to take on the role of the king of instruments.

Bartók's concerto is a difficult work but it's also very beautiful and effective, although in live performance there's always a problem of balance, as it's hard for a viola to produce a big enough sound. Bartók left the concerto unfinished when he died but I like the colouristic orchestration of Tibor Serly's completion: he lived at the same time as Bartók, so it has a certain authority.'

PROM 28

Joshua Bell plays
Sibelius Violin Concerto

'The Sibelius Violin Concerto has a very dark quality, quite unlike any other violin concerto that I know. I began studying it when I was 15 and it's been in my repertory ever since, but I still think it's one of the most moving violin pieces ever written. People tend to pigeon-hole Sibelius as a composer who only wrote about Finland and landscapes, but that's wrong. In the work's wonderful central slow movement, he produces music that is full of passion and emotion – very human music. But it's also a very taxing and athletic work, and takes a lot of energy and strength to play. Even Heifetz, whose recording was the first version of the piece I ever heard, apparently admitted he found it particularly difficult.

I'm looking forward to playing it at the Proms. The Royal Albert Hall is one of my favourite venues, and this concerto is a particularly good piece to play there: it's a big work that needs a big space as well as a real feeling of intimacy.'

PROM 43

Alfred Brendel plays
Beethoven Piano Concerto No. 5
in E flat major, 'Emperor'

'Beethoven's Fifth Concerto was the first work I performed publicly with an orchestra, when I was aged 17. The nickname 'Emperor' has always struck me as inappropriate; 'Anti-Emperor' would be more to the point, as it was composed in 1809, around the time that Napoleon's troops invaded Vienna. For me, the concerto must be taken as a hymn to liberty, a vision of victory over violence and oppression.

The character of the work is entirely positive. I have always delighted in the mixture of grandeur and enthusiasm in the outer movements, as well as in the radiant introspection of the *Adagio un poco mosso*, of which Beethoven's pupil Czerny says that it must not drag.

I look forward to playing the concerto that initiated my career in my ultimate Prom. Although I have stopped performing for live broadcasts, I agreed to make an exception for this concert, because it will also contain new settings, by Harrison Birtwistle, of three of my own poems. I can't wait to hear them.'

PROM 59

Hélène Grimaud plays
Brahms Piano Concerto No. 1

'Brahms's First Piano Concerto is a piece that's vital to my existence; that's how strongly I feel about it, and how connected I am to it. It's an intensely dramatic and emotional work that can be both introspective and in a state of revolt, and from a structural standpoint I feel there is something very raw and extremely spontaneous in the way the material appears. People tend to have preconceived ideas about Brahms and who he was. They always think of that picture of him as an older man, but in his letters Schumann describes Brahms's impetuous nature; there was this vital force about him, something irrepressible, and that's something a lot of people don't seem to perceive in his music.

Every pianist has a different physical approach to the piano and a different physiology that determines what is easier for them to play. Although there is a lot for the pianist to do in the Brahms concerto – the material is extremely rich and full of wonderful contrasts – for me it just feels so organic that technical considerations don't really come into it. It's music I've always felt resonates intensely with my inner world, that I feel very close to.'

PROM 52

Dmitri Hvorostovsky sings
Musorgsky Songs and Dances of Death

'When I first performed at the Proms, back in 1993, I sang these very same Musorgsky songs, so for me it's a great opportunity to be able to sing them again this year, and to see how my understanding and interpretation of them has changed over the years.

The *Songs and Dances of Death* is one of the toughest cycles ever written, in terms both of its vocal difficulties and of the dramatic demands of the texts. It's a very complex cycle, dark and moody. The second song, 'Serenade', can stand alone as a separate work or encore – it has beautiful melodies that really stick in your mind. The 'Trepak' is very dramatic: the great Russian bass Fyodor Chaliapin was particularly fond of it. The most challenging song, though, is the last, 'The Field-Marshal', which I sing in an extremely high key in order to create that almost squeaky sound of the top register. The many high G naturals here are at the limits of the baritone range and you really have to be on top form to get it right. It's a fantastic piece when you do!'

PROM 7

Magdalena Kožená sings
Novák Melancholic Songs of Love

'Although I've sung other pieces by Novák in the past, I only recently discovered his *Melancholic Songs of Love*. I knew they existed in a piano version but not that he had actually orchestrated them himself.

Finding pieces by Czech composers for my kind of voice and orchestra is difficult, because the music is generally quite heavy; even this cycle is quite a challenge for me. But I love to present new or unheard-of pieces, and these songs are so special, I'm very happy to have the chance to sing them. I also love the texts, which are quite sad. But we Slavs do tend to enjoy this kind of sadness!

The first song has an especially powerful text, telling how one day love was born and knocked on the door of the people, and how everyone refused to accept it; how they were afraid of it, and tried to protect themselves from real emotions. All this is wonderfully described in the music, and in Novák's colourful late-Romantic orchestration, which sometimes reminds me of Puccini.

The real challenge is to tell the story, though, which is difficult when the audience doesn't understand the language. I can never decide if it's better for them to read the text in translation, in which case they can't concentrate on what's going on on stage, or just to listen to the lovely music but have no idea what you're singing about!'

PROM 38

Cynthia Millar plays
Messiaen Turangalîla Symphony

'As an ondes martenot player, *Turangalîla* is one of the absolute staples of my repertoire. Even though I've been playing it since 1986, I still really love it. In fact, the first time I ever played it was at the Proms, with the National Youth Orchestra and Mark Elder, but I've played it so often since then, well over 50 times, that I've now lost count!

There are actually many places in *Turangalîla* where it's hard for a listener to

pick the ondes line out – its role is very often just a matter of adding a lovely colouring to other sounds. Probably the first time that an audience can really identify me and the instrument, and what it is that we're doing, is also one of my favourite bits: it comes soon after the start of the second movement, when the ondes comes in with a very beautiful line supported by the strings. But the bit I really love is my final page of music, where Messiaen wrote a whole series of crazy trills that go all the way up the instrument. He asks for them to be played with the 'ruban' (ribbon), the sliding device, which means that they come out a bit wilder than they would if I was just playing them on the keyboard. It's very joyful and amazing, and really fun to play.'

PROM 45

Willard W. White sings the role of Wotan in
Wagner Das Rheingold

'Wotan is Wagner's human expression of a god. Singing the role is fascinating – it's a chance to get a taste of Wagner's mind, and to marry that to my mind to create a new interpretation of the character, to bring him to life in a completely different way. This, for me, is part of the magic. To perform the role convincingly I have to totally believe in the words I am singing – I have to believe that I am going to get Valhalla built, come hell or high water.

In opera you have to use your imagination, especially in a concert performance, when there are no sets or props to work with, only the motivation and inspiration that the music conjures up. Of course, that sort of inspiration also depends on who is conducting, and how the music is being played and sung, and all these different elements are unpredictable in a way, so you make a guess and commit yourself to it, and the words and music just guide you.

An opera like *Das Rheingold* can be exhausting for the performer, as the emotion and drama involves the whole body and mind. It also means being on your feet for two and a half hours! But, for me, the pleasure in what I'm doing negates the tiredness and makes it all worthwhile.'

BBC New Generation Artists

The BBC's New Generation Artists scheme started five years ago. **Adam Gatehouse**, its Executive Producer, explains how it works; **Louise Downes** talks to the four young participants appearing in this year's Proms

The New Generation Artists scheme was launched by Radio 3 in the autumn of 1999 as part of its commitment to young artists. It offers them unique opportunities to develop their talents across the network. These include lunchtime concerts in both London and beyond, appearances and recordings with the BBC orchestras, special studio recordings for Radio 3 and, last but not least, appearances at the Proms.

Several New Generation Artists have made successful CDs in co-productions with EMI's *Debut* series, three of which – by the Belcea Quartet, Jonathan Lemalu and Simon Trpčeski – have won *Gramophone* Awards as 'Best Debut CD of the Year'; others have recorded cover CDs for *BBC Music Magazine*. New Generation Artists also feature regularly at Britain's major festivals.

Each year six new soloists or groups are recruited for a two-year period. There are thus 12 active New Generation Artists at any one time, representing a real cross-section of the most exciting young British and international musical talent.

Looking back over the first five years of the scheme, it's thrilling to see how all the artists have now become part of the fabric of the international music scene. The stars of tomorrow very much in evidence today!

PROM 2

Jonathan Lemalu sings popular arias in 'The Nation's Favourite Prom'

'The first time I sang at the Proms was on the First Night in 2001. For a young student still at college, it was pretty cool being one of the 16 'leading young singers' picked to perform in Vaughan Williams's *Serenade to Music*. The next year I sang Don Quixote in Falla's *Master Peter's Puppet Show* at a Late Night Prom. That was quite a contrast from the atmosphere of a First Night. Then last year was my year for ghosts and voices. Not only did I make my Glyndebourne debut as the Voice of Neptune in Mozart's *Idomeneo*, but I sang at the Proms as both the Ghost of Samuel [in Handel's *Saul*] and the Ghost of Hector [in Berlioz's *The Trojans*] – on consecutive days! As Hector, Colin Davis banished me up to the organ loft: I don't know whether it was because of my singing or just for sound-balance, but I sort of felt I'd found my niche up there, looking down on this stadium full of people. There's something about the Royal Albert Hall – it has such mystique.

Being an NGA has been an incredible experience. At first you're just so happy to be part of it all – but pretty soon you're hanging on for dear life! There's just so much new repertoire you have to learn, it's almost a case of sensory overload. But I love it!'

PROM 55

Sally Matthews sings the role of Lauretta in **Puccini** Gianni Schicchi

'Whenever I tell people that I'm doing *Gianni Schicchi*, their faces usually just go blank. But I only have to hum the tune of 'O my beloved daddy', and they all go 'Ah! That one!' It must be one of the best-known tunes in all opera.

I first sang the piece when I was still at the Guildhall. It was actually a very good choice for a student show. It's a real ensemble work, in which everyone gets a chance to shine – though of course, as Lauretta, I do get to sing the most popular number! Because it's such a lovely tune, it's often taken far too slowly. But it's a very simple thing that she's doing, after all – twisting her father round her little finger. I do it to my own dad all the time!

I'm really looking forward to singing it at Glyndebourne. It's the first time I'll have worked down there. Even better, my husband Tom [Watmough] plays the clarinet in the London Philharmonic, so he'll be in the orchestra! We've actually just recorded Schubert's *The Shepherd on the Rock* together, as part of my debut disc for EMI. That's one of the many fantastic things that's come out of being on the scheme.'

Sally Matthews also gives a joint recital with Ailish Tynan in PCM 3

PCM 3

Ailish Tynan sings songs and duets by **Strauss** and **Dvořák**

PCM 4

Llŷr Williams plays piano works by **Chopin**, **Debussy**, **Janáček** and **Skryabin**

Former New Generation Artists appearing this season:

'It's been wonderful to have the opportunity to sing with all the BBC orchestras – Samuel Barber's *Knoxville* up in Glasgow with the BBC Scottish, Ravel's *Shéhérazade* with the BBC Philharmonic in Manchester, and so on. But it's a lot of hard work too, that's for sure. I did a couple of song recitals at the very beginning of my stint and virtually used up all of my repertoire! People don't want to hear you singing the same things all the time, so I've had to learn a lot of new stuff. I've probably learnt about 35 new songs just in the past two months. I'll probably never have to learn another song in my whole career!

I'm really looking forward to my joint recital with Sally [Matthews]. She and I are great friends. We were both Vilar Young Artists at the Royal Opera House and sang in Dvořák's *Rusalka* together there, so it will be great to sing some of his *Moravian Duets* with her as well. As for Strauss, he's my all-time favourite composer. His wife was a singer, of course, so he wrote beautifully for the voice. If ever I'm giving a really important recital, I always try to stick in a couple of his songs – especially *Morgen*. It's my lucky song. I'm sure it's what won me the Recital Prize in last year's BBC Singer of the World in Cardiff.'

Ailish Tynan also sings in Vivaldi's 'Gloria' in Prom 47

'Becoming a New Generation Artist has been one of the best things that's ever happened to me career-wise. Obviously it gives you lots of opportunities to be heard, but it's also good to be forced to learn new pieces – they're always asking for new repertoire. And it's good too to have the opportunity to work with some of the other NGAs. For instance, this summer I'm doing a recording of the Messiaen *Quartet for the End of Time* with Martin Fröst [on clarinet], Janine Jansen [violin] and Claudio Bohórquez [cello].

I'm really quite pleased with the programme we've come up with for my V&A recital: two long pieces, with two cycles of shorter pieces in between. It begins with a bang with one of Chopin's most exciting, virtuosic, and almost demonic, pieces. Then we have music by Debussy and Skryabin, two composers who were influenced by Chopin and were both, like him, explorers in terms of sonic possibilities. And then there's Janáček, who was an explorer too, of course, and one of the most individual voices of the 20th century. I've also tried to make connections between the works. Thus the last piece of Debussy's *Estampes*, which is called 'Gardens in the Rain', is followed by Janáček's *In the Mists*. And I'll end with the Fifth Sonata by Skryabin. He's probably my favourite Russian composer – his harmonies are just so interesting.'

PROM 47

Emma Bell sings **Vivaldi** Gloria **Arne** Artaxerxes – three arias

PCM 7

Emily Beynon plays **Messiaen** Le merle noir

PROM 18

Alice Coote sings **Mahler** Kindertotenlieder

PROM 18

Paul Lewis plays **Mozart** Piano Concerto No. 23 in A major, K488

PROM 54

Christopher Maltman sings the role of Death in **Holst** Sāvitri

PROM 45

James Rutherford sings the role of Donner in **Wagner** Das Rheingold

PROM 15

Simon Trpčeski plays **Saint-Saëns** Piano Concerto No. 2 in G minor

BBC Symphony Orchestra

'A unique and unforgettable experience'
The Guardian

2004–2005 Barbican Season

A series of concerts featuring a range of music to tempt every palate, including works from some of today's foremost composers, performed by an impressive line-up of guests.

Highlights include

John Adams Major works conducted by the composer, including *Harmonium*

James MacMillan The featured composer in the 2005 January Composer Weekend

Two major twentieth-century operas:
Tippett *The Knot Garden*
In celebration of the 100th anniversary of the birth of Sir Michael Tippett

Harrison Birtwistle *The Second Mrs Kong**
Part of *Birtwistle Games: A celebration of Harrison Birtwistle* at the South Bank Centre from 20 Oct to 11 Nov 2004. For details see www.rfh.org.uk/birtwistle

Mahler Symphony No 2 with Christine Brewer and Petra Lang, and **Strauss** *Drei Hymnen* with Christine Brewer

Mozart Requiem, with the BBC Symphony Chorus

Ravel *Shéhérazade* and **Debussy/Adams** *Baudelaire Songs* performed by Susan Graham

Sibelius Violin Concerto, with Leonidas Kavakos

World premieres of BBC commissions from:
Richard Barrett, Lyell Cresswell, Brett Dean

Conductors include:
Jukka-Pekka Saraste, Sir Andrew Davis, John Adams, Jiří Bělohlávek, Martyn Brabbins, Paavo Järvi, Oliver Knussen, James MacMillan, Tadaaki Otaka, Donald Runnicles, Yan Pascal Tortelier

Save on ticket prices by becoming a BBC SO subscriber. Tickets available in June.
Call the Barbican Box Office on 020 7638 8891 from June for a free brochure with details of all events.

barbican

Box Office
020 7638 8891 (bkg fee)
www.barbican.org.uk
Reduced booking fee online

Tickets £16 £12 £8

* Different ticket prices apply

BBC RADIO 3 90-93 FM

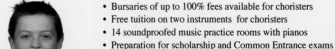
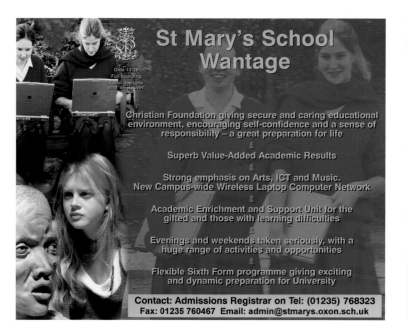

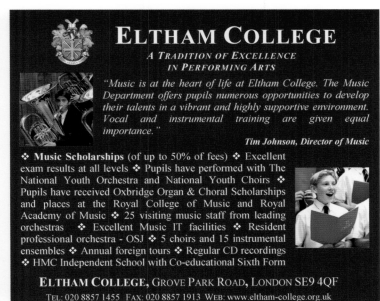
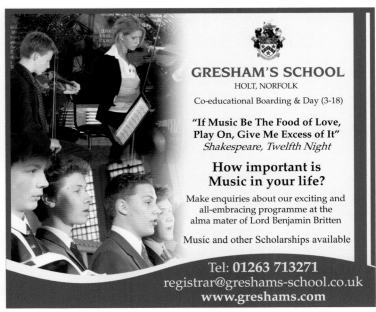

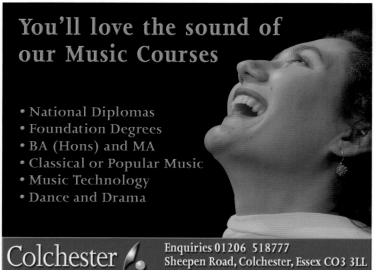

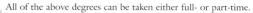

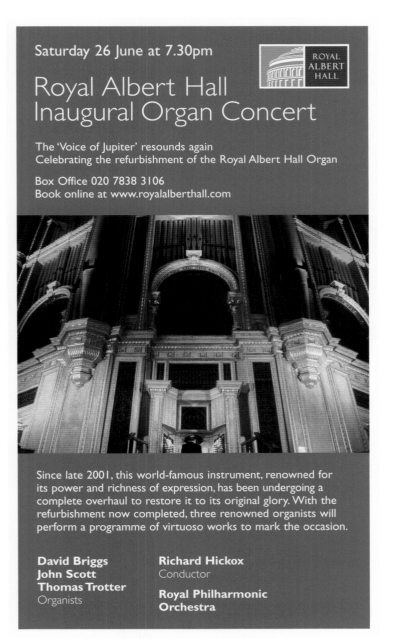

RAH ORGAN

RESTORED!

All swell that ends well

Following the completion of the Royal Albert Hall development, **Adrian Jack** welcomes the return to action of 'Father' Willis's organ

LEFT, RIGHT & FAR RIGHT
The restored Royal Albert
Hall organ reclaims its
historic status as the UK's
largest concert instrument

ABOVE
Naji Hakim, Olivier Messiaen's
successor as organist at
La Trinité church in Paris

For two seasons, Prommers have missed the sound of the mighty Royal Albert Hall organ and made do with electronic substitutes. The real thing, fully restored in all its glory, launches this year's season with the familiar flourishes of Bach's Toccata in D minor (with the Fugue following in the 1929 orchestration that Henry Wood passed off under the pseudonym 'Paul Klenovsky'). The job of restoring the organ has cost £1.7 million and represents the last lap of the Hall's eight-year programme of building and restoration, at a total cost of £70 million.

Prommers last heard the Royal Albert Hall organ when Wayne Marshall played a Messiaen sequence in the 2001 season. Messiaen features again this season, when Naji Hakim, the composer's successor as organist at La Trinité in Paris, plays another selection of the Master's works, enabling us to hear some of the organ's subtler, quieter stops.

When Henry ('Father') Willis finished the organ in 1871, it was the largest in the world, with 111 stops distributed over four manuals and pedals. The main pipes of the Great Organ were placed in the central arch of the case – and still are – with the upper pedal pipes in the arches each side. Steam engines drove the

blowers. This was the instrument played by such distinguished visitors as Anton Bruckner and Camille Saint-Saëns.

Willis was criticised in his day for making organs that were too brash and brilliant – he had, after all, been to France and studied the 'orchestral' organs of Aristide Cavaillé-Coll. Yet his Albert Hall instrument, which helped establish him as the most famous English organ-builder of his day, was found wanting in power to fill the farthest reaches of its vast home.

Taste and fashion in organ design change, too, and by the 1920s there was a will to improve Willis's organ. The job was given to the Durham firm of Harrison & Harrison, who, because of difficulties in fund-raising, completed it in two stages. The result, unveiled early in 1934, was a transformed and enlarged organ, with 146 stops and 9,779 pipes, the greatest number in the country. The blowing system was electric (costing about two shillings and six pence an hour, or 12 and a half pence in today's currency) and the action electro-pneumatic, except for mechanical manual-to-pedal couplers. This was the organ that many people will remember, played on so many memorable occasions by such popular favourites as Marcel Dupré (who gave his last public recital on the instrument, at the age of 85) and George Thalben-Ball, the instrument's curator from 1934 until his death in 1987.

In the 1970s further changes were made, including the removal of the unenclosed Choir pipes to a position behind the console, which was also refurbished with new keyboards.

But by the end of the century, the increasing decrepitude of the organ (Harrison's had to be on call each time it was played) prompted radical remedies, and tenders were invited, both from this country and abroad, for its restoration. The judging committee included the Royal Albert Hall's Director of Building Development, the organists John Birch (Thalben-Ball's successor as curator) and Nicolas Kynaston, as well as two organ-building experts, Nicholas Thistlethwaite and Ian Bell. The contract was awarded to Mander Organs of London.

They decided that it was out of the question to return to Willis's original 1871 instrument, since it was only possible to guess what it had sounded like, and the original organ would have been ill-suited to today's needs anyway. So essentially what has been restored is the Harrison organ of 70 years ago. Most of the work has involved replacing the mechanism behind the scenes, with only minor stop changes, a further modification to the position of the Choir division (now placed a bit higher than before, behind a grille) and the addition of 220 extra pipes, bringing the total number to 9,999 and restoring the Royal Albert Hall organ to its historic status as the largest in the UK.

For many years people complained that the organ was too seldom played for its own sake, and only ever summoned to drown out the riotous booing at boxing matches. But now that the restoration is complete, the 'Voice of Jupiter' can once again resound in its own right.

Royal Albert Hall development update

The £70m, eight-year programme of improvements to the RAH was completed earlier this year. This year's Proms audiences will notice the following principal changes since last summer:
• Improvements to the external setting of the Hall, including new York stone paving, and to the traffic islands and street furniture
• New floodlighting to illuminate the upper part of the Hall and the South Porch, with special coloured lighting for the mosaic
• Final redecoration of the upper auditorium and Gallery
• New shop in the South Porch and daytime access to the Café Consort. *For full details of eating and drinking facilities at the Hall, and of the new accompanied tours of the building, see pages 124–5*
The Development was made possible through significant grants from the Arts Council and Heritage Lottery Funds and the generosity of charitable trusts, individual benefactors and the Hall's seat-holders. The Hall is particularly grateful to the many Proms-goers who contributed via the audience appeal or the collection made by the Prommers last season.

BELOW
9,997 ... 9,998 ... 9,999 – all pipes present and correct!

Organ music at the Proms

Bach	Toccata and Fugue in D minor	Prom 1	Janáček	Glagolitic Mass	Prom 16
				Our Father	Prom 48
Barber	Toccata festiva	Prom 74	MacMillan	Le tombeau de Georges Rouault	Prom 48
Bingham	The Secret Garden	Prom 48			
Britten	Voluntary on Tallis's Lamentations;		Messiaen	Messe de la Pentecôte – Les langues de feu, Le vent de l'Esprit; Offrande au Saint-Sacrement; La nativité du Seigneur – Dieu parmi nous	Prom 34
	War Requiem	Prom 22			
Dvořák	Mass in D	Prom 13			
Eben	Sunday Music – Moto ostinato	Prom 48	Saint-Saëns	Symphony No. 3 in C minor, 'Organ'	Prom 39
Hakim	Ouverture libanaise; Organo, chordis et choro	Prom 34	Taverner	In nomine	Prom 14

BOOKING

How to book

Your copy of the *BBC Proms 2004 Guide* contains a tear-out form for Priority Booking. For your best chance of securing the tickets you want, fill it in and post or fax it to arrive at the Royal Albert Hall Box Office by Monday 17 May.

You can also use the Online Ticket Request system for Priority Booking.
Visit the BBC Proms website for details:
www.bbc.co.uk/proms

The Box Office will begin processing bookings on Monday 17 May; all bookings received before this date will be treated as if they had arrived on that day. All Priority Bookings, whether sent by post, fax or online, are processed simultaneously and no method receives preference. Note that the Online Ticket Request option is not a 'real time' booking system.

Express Bookings will be handled first – for full details see page 129.

Note that until General Booking opens on Monday 14 June, only bookings made on the official Priority Booking Form or via the Online Ticket Request system will be accepted.

The Last Night of the Proms
Because of the high demand for tickets, special booking arrangements apply. See page 127

Special Offers
For Special Offers, see overleaf

Priority Booking
By post, fax and online – opens Monday 17 May
Use the Priority Booking Form or visit www.bbc.co.uk/proms

To take advantage of the Priority Booking period – and enjoy your best chance of securing the seats you want – use the official Priority Booking Form (facing page 130) or visit the Proms website. Note that all postal, fax and online bookings received before Monday 17 May will be treated as if they had arrived on that date.

Postal address: BBC Proms, Box Office, Royal Albert Hall, London SW7 2AP
Fax: 020 7581 9311   **Online booking: www.bbc.co.uk/proms**

General Booking
In person, by phone or online – opens Monday 14 June

The Box Office is located at Door 12 of the Royal Albert Hall and is open 9.00am–9.00pm daily. Note that no booking fee applies to tickets bought in person at the Hall.

Telephone: 020 7589 8212   **Online booking: www.bbc.co.uk/proms**

Last Night Ballot
Exclusive to readers of the *BBC Proms 2004 Guide*

Your chance to enter this year's Last Night Ballot and apply for tickets to the Last Night. See page 127.

Promming on the Day
Don't book, just turn up

Up to 1,400 standing places are available at each concert. Weekend Promming Passes and Season Tickets can be booked in advance: see pages 98 and 123. Additionally, over 500 Arena and Gallery tickets are always on sale at the door from an hour beforehand, so you can just turn up on the night.

Special Offers

Same Day Savers

Book for more than one concert on the same day, and save £4.00 on your ticket for the later concert.

Note: offer applies to matinée, evening and late night performances in the Royal Albert Hall. Not valid for Arena, Gallery and Circle (Restricted View) price areas.

Under-16s

The Proms are a great way to discover live music, and we encourage anyone over 5 years old to attend. Tickets for Under-16s can be purchased at half-price in any seating area for the following Proms:

2, 8, 10, 12, 19, 24, 25, 31, 38, 39, 40, 42, 46, 47, 49, 50, 59, 62, 63, 66, 70

The *Blue Peter* Proms (Prom 10 & Prom 12) are expressly designed to introduce children to concert-going, while the other concerts have been highlighted because they include music that will appeal to the younger audience.

Group Bookings

Group booking rates now apply to all Proms except the Last Night (Prom 74). Groups of 10 or more can claim a 10% discount on the price of Centre/Side Stalls or Front/Rear Circle tickets for all Proms in the A, B, D, E and G price bands, and a 5% discount for C band concerts.

For more information, call the Group Booking Information Line: 020 7838 3108. Please note that for security reasons group purchases can only be made online during the Priority Booking period. This offer is subject to availability.

Weekend Promming Pass

Beat the queues at the weekend and save money! In addition to discounted tickets, the Weekend Promming Pass offers guaranteed access up to 10 minutes before start-time to the Arena or Gallery standing areas for all concerts in the Royal Albert Hall on Fridays, Saturdays and Sundays (excluding Proms 10, 12, 73 and 74). Passes can be purchased in advance – by post or fax (using the Priority Booking Form) or online, and (from Monday 14 June) by phone or in person at the Box Office up to 6.00pm on Friday nights (5.30pm on 6 August, 20 August and 3 September). Prices vary for each weekend depending on the number of concerts.

Note that Weekend 2 excludes the *Blue Peter* Proms; Weekend 7 includes Bank Holiday Monday (30 August); and there is no pass covering Proms 73 and 74.

Passes are non-transferable and signature ID may be requested upon entry. Purchase of a Weekend Pass does not guarantee entry to the Last Night, but tickets may be counted towards the 'Six Concert Rule' (see page 127) in conjunction with further Passes or Day Ticket stubs.

Note that you may only purchase a maximum of four passes per weekend (subject to availability)

For whole/half season Season Tickets, see page 123

Weekend Promming Pass prices		
Weekend 1	Proms 1–3	£10
Weekend 2	Proms 9, 11 & 13	£10
Weekend 3	Proms 19–23	£18
Weekend 4	Proms 29–32	£14
Weekend 5	Proms 38–41	£14
Weekend 6	Proms 46–49	£14
Weekend 7	Proms 56–60	£18
Weekend 8	Proms 64–67	£14

All offers are subject to availability. Offers and discounts may not be combined.

PROM 1

Friday 16 July
7.30pm – c9.45pm
Price Code **B**

PROM 2

Saturday 17 July
7.00pm – c9.20pm
Price Code **A**

  NOTE TIME

Bach/Henry Wood
Toccata* and Fugue in D minor   9'

Elgar
The Music Makers   40'

interval

Holst
The Planets   50'

Lorraine Hunt Lieberson
mezzo-soprano
Martin Neary *organ**

BBC Symphony Chorus
BBC Symphony Orchestra
Leonard Slatkin conductor

Holst's ever-popular planetary trip and a choral ode by Elgar that quotes from several of his best-known works launch the 2004 Proms – and this year's English music theme. Chief Conductor Leonard Slatkin conducts the BBC Symphony Chorus and Orchestra, acclaimed American mezzo-soprano Lorraine Hunt Lieberson returns to the Proms, and we welcome back the newly-restored Royal Albert Hall organ in a famous Toccata twinned with an orchestration of its Fugue by Proms founder-conductor Henry Wood.

📖 *England at the Crossroads,*
pages 32–8; Restored!, pages 94–6

This concert will be broadcast on BBC2

The Nation's Favourite Prom

Overture
Chosen by you – see *panel*

Delius
A Village Romeo and Juliet –
The Walk to the Paradise Garden 10'

Mozart
The Marriage of Figaro – 'Non
più andrai'   4'

Don Giovanni – 'Madamina,
il catalogo è questo'   5'

Rakhmaninov
Rhapsody on a Theme of Paganini 22'

interval

Overture
Chosen by you – see *panel*

Boito
Mefistofele –
'Son lo spirito che nega'   4'

Gounod
Faust – 'Vous qui faites l'endormie';
'Le veau d'or'   5'

Tchaikovsky
Overture '1812'   15'

Jonathan Lemalu *bass-baritone*
Louis Lortie *piano*

Hallé Orchestra
Mark Elder conductor

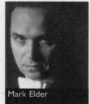

Mark Elder

The Hallé was the first out-of-London orchestra ever to appear at the Proms, and their fortunes have recently prospered in a dynamic partnership with Mark Elder. You, the audience, have the chance to choose two overtures in this popular programme, which also includes favourite arias, sung by BBC New Generation Artist Jonathan Lemalu, a familiar set of variations featuring Canadian pianist Louis Lortie, and one of the best-loved orchestral works by Delius, the third of 2004's English anniversary composers. The whole evening ends with a bang, in the form of Tchaikovsky's cannonading victory celebration.

📖 *England at the Crossroads,*
pages 32–8

This concert will be broadcast on BBC1

To vote for your favourite overture, choose from the following shortlist. Two of the favourites will be included in the concert, and everyone who votes will have the chance to win tickets to the concert too.

1.   **Beethoven** Egmont
2.   **Berlioz** Roman Carnival
3.   **Glinka** Ruslan and Lyudmila
4.   **Mendelssohn** Hebrides
5.   **Mozart** Marriage of Figaro
6.   **Nicolai**
     Merry Wives of Windsor
7.   **Rossini** William Tell
8.   **Rossini** Thieving Magpie
9.   **Smetana** Bartered Bride
10. **J. Strauss II** Fledermaus
11. **Verdi** Force of Destiny
12. **Weber** Freischütz

There are three ways to vote:
• online at www.bbc.co.uk/proms (where you can listen to sound-clips)

• by telephone on 09066 800 601 (calls cost 25p a minute)

• by SMS: text PROMS plus the first word of your chosen overture's title, eg. 'PROMS EGMONT', to 83111 (messages cost a maximum of 12p)

Voting closes at 12.00 midnight on Monday 21 June

PROM 3

Sunday 18 July
6.30pm – c10.20pm
Price Code **A**

Dvořák
Dimitrij
(concert performance; sung in Czech) 190'

Stuart Skelton *Dimitrij Ivanovič*
Elena Prokina *Marina Mníškova*
Krassimira Stoyanova *Xenie Borisovna*
Dagmar Pecková *Marfa Ivanovna*
Dalibor Jenis *Prince Vasilij Šujský*
Manfred Hemm
Jov, the Patriarch of Moscow
Peter Coleman-Wright
Petr Fedorovič Basmanov
Jared Holt *Něborský*

Slovak Philharmonic Choir
BBC National Orchestra of Wales
Richard Hickox *conductor*

A major operatic revival to mark the
100th anniversary of the death of
Dvořák. His grand opera *Dimitrij* picks
up the thread of Russian history where
Musorgsky's *Boris Godunov* leaves off.
The BBC National Orchestra of Wales
and Principal Conductor Richard Hickox
are joined by a Slovak choir and an
international cast, with rising Australian
tenor Stuart Skelton making his Proms
debut in the demanding title-role.

📖 *Back to Bohemia, pages 18–23*

There will be one interval

💬 **5.00pm Pre-Prom Talk** (RAH)
Piers Burton-Page

PROM 4

Monday 19 July
7.00pm – c9.05pm
Price Code **A**

BBC4.

Elgar
Cockaigne   12'
Delius
Sea Drift   26'

interval

Holst
The Hymn of Jesus   23'
Elgar
Enigma Variations   30'

Thomas Hampson *baritone*

BBC National Chorus of Wales
The Bach Choir
Choir of St Paul's Cathedral
BBC National Orchestra of Wales
Richard Hickox *conductor*

The three great British composers who
died in 1934 come together: American
baritone Thomas Hampson is the
soloist in Delius's masterly setting of
verse by the great American poet Walt
Whitman; while Holst's mystical *Hymn
of Jesus* offers the Eastern-influenced
composer's ecstatic, dance-led
response to an ancient Christian text.

📖 *England at the Crossroads,
pages 32–8*

This concert will be broadcast on BBC4

🎵 **1.00pm Proms Chamber Music**
See pages 120–21
💬 **5.30pm Pre-Prom Talk** (RCM)
Nicholas Kenyon and Richard Hickox

PROM 5

Monday 19 July
10.00pm – c11.20pm
Price Code **D**

Dallapiccola
Canti di prigionia   25'
Ockeghem, arr. Birtwistle
Ut heremita solus   7'
Sir Harrison Birtwistle
The Ring Dance of the Nazarene 26'
BBC/VARA co-commission: UK premiere

Roderick Williams *baritone*
Martin Allen *percussion*

BBC Singers
Endymion
Stephen Cleobury *conductor*

The first work in our 70th birthday
celebration for Sir Harrison Birtwistle
is also the first of this year's UK
premieres: *The Ring Dance of the
Nazarene*, a characteristically ritualistic
work written for the charismatic young
baritone Roderick Williams. The BBC
Singers under Chief Conductor
Stephen Cleobury also celebrate the
centenary of Luigi Dallapiccola with his
set of three 'prison choruses'
composed in protest at the rise of
Fascism in pre-war Italy.

📖 *England at the Crossroads,
pages 32–8; New Music, pages 46–52*

There will be no interval

PROM 6

Tuesday 20 July
7.30pm – c9.35pm
Price Code **A**

BBC4

Zhou Long
The Immortal   c15'
*BBC World Service commission:
world premiere*

Liszt
Piano Concerto No. 2 in A major 21'

interval

R. Strauss
An Alpine Symphony   50'

Jean-Yves Thibaudet *piano*

BBC Symphony Orchestra
Leonard Slatkin *conductor*

Jean-Yves Thibaudet

Strauss's
resplendent *Alpine
Symphony*
represents the
peak of the
composer's
symphonic
endeavours, Liszt's lyrical and virtuosic
Second Piano Concerto is performed
by Proms favourite Jean-Yves
Thibaudet, and the first of this year's
world premieres, commissioned by the
BBC World Service, highlights our
East/West theme.

📖 *EAST/WEST, pages 4–12*

This concert will be broadcast on BBC4

🎵 **6.00pm Composer Portrait**
Zhou Long. See page 144

PROM 7 — Wednesday 21 July
7.30pm – c9.40pm
Price Code **A**

BBC4

Vejvanovský
Sonata vespertina a 8   8'

Mysliveček
L'Olimpiade –
'Che non mi disse un di!'   3'

Mozart
'Vado, ma dove?', K583   4'
'Alma grande e nobil core', K578   5'

Martinů
Double Concerto for piano,
timpani and strings   22'

interval

Novák
Melancholic Songs of Love   10'

Mozart
Symphony No. 38 in D major,
K504 'Prague'   28'

Magdalena Kožená mezzo-soprano
Marcel Javorček piano
Pavel Rehberger timpani

Prague Philharmonia
Jiří Bělohlávek conductor

A star Czech mezzo-soprano joins
her compatriot Jiří Bělohlávek and his
Prague Philharmonia in music highlighting
the links between Mozart and Prague.

Back to Bohemia, pages 18–23;
Proms Artists, pages 80–85

This concert will be broadcast on BBC4

💬 **6.00pm Pre-Prom Talk** (RCM)
Jan Smaczny

PROM 8 — Thursday 22 July
7.30pm – c9.50pm
Price Code **A**

BBC4

John Casken
Symphony 'Broken Consort'   c35'
BBC commission: world premiere

Ravel
Piano Concerto in G major   22'

interval

Stravinsky
The Firebird   47'

Pierre-Laurent Aimard piano

BBC Philharmonic
Gianandrea Noseda conductor

Gianandrea Noseda

Stravinsky's *The Firebird* launches our 75th-anniversary tribute to the great Russian ballet impresario Serge Diaghilev. John Casken's *Broken Consort* was composed for the versatile talents hidden within the BBC Philharmonic. Ravel's effervescent, jazzy concerto features the brilliant French pianist Pierre-Laurent Aimard *(see also PCM 7)*.

New Music, pages 46–52;
Season Highlights, page 61;
Proms Artists, pages 80–85

This concert will be broadcast on BBC4

🎵 **6.00pm Composer Portrait**
John Casken. See page 144

PROM 9 — Friday 23 July
7.30pm – c10.05pm
Price Code **A**

BBC4

De Grigny, orch. Benjamin
Livre d'orgue – Récit de tierce
en taille   5'
world premiere

George Benjamin
Palimpsest I and II   20'

interval

Messiaen
Des canyons aux étoiles …   95'

Ueli Wiget piano
Simon Breyer horn
Rumi Ogawa xylorimba
Rainer Römer glockenspiel

Ensemble Modern
George Benjamin conductor

Composer-conductor George Benjamin launches this season's survey of the major orchestral works of his teacher, Olivier Messiaen. The awe-inspiring cycle of meditations on the majesty of God, as revealed in a visit to the canyons of Utah, is prefaced by Benjamin's own exquisite pair of *Palimpsests* and his new orchestration of a striking Baroque organ work.

Season Highlights, page 62

This concert will be broadcast on BBC4

💬 **6.00pm Pre-Prom Talk** (RAH)
George Benjamin

PROM 10 — Saturday 24 July
11.00am – c1.00pm
Price Code **G**

**Blue Peter Prom – Beating
Drums, Dancing Lions**

Liz Barker presenter
Simon Thomas presenter

Kagemusha Taiko drummers
Choy Lee Fut Kung Fu School

City of Birmingham Youth Chorus
BBC Philharmonic
Gianandrea Noseda conductor
Jason Lai conductor

We conjure up the spectacular sights and sounds of the Far East as two special groups of performers join *Blue Peter* presenters Simon and Liz and the BBC Philharmonic for an exotic and colourful programme inspired by the season's EAST/WEST theme. The big Japanese drums of Kagemusha Taiko and the traditional Chinese costumes of the Choy Lee Fut Kung Fu School Lion Dance troupe will be seen at the Proms for the first time. You can thrill to the power of the Royal Albert Hall's organ in Strauss's *Also sprach Zarathustra* (you know it as *2001: A Space Odyssey!*) and hear the orchestra in fantastic dance music by Tchaikovsky, Ravel and Stravinsky. And after a favourite theme from *Harry Potter*, everyone can join in with the orchestra and the City of Birmingham Youth Chorus in a taste of the familiar festivities of the Last Night of the Proms, by singing 'Land of Hope and Glory'.

There will be one interval

PROM 11

Saturday 24 July
7.30pm – c9.35pm
Price Code **A**

BBC4

Bernstein
Chichester Psalms   19'

Ives
Symphony No. 4   33'

interval

Stravinsky
Petrushka (1947 version)   34'

David Stark treble

City of Birmingham Symphony Chorus
City of Birmingham Symphony Orchestra
Sakari Oramo conductor

The CBSO adventurously gave a complete Charles Ives symphony cycle in Birmingham last season. Sakari Oramo now brings the huge Fourth Symphony to the Proms to mark the 50th anniversary of Ives's death. Stravinsky's puppet ballet *Petrushka* continues our 75th-anniversary tribute to Diaghilev, and the lively mix is completed by Leonard Bernstein's infectiously rhythmic Hebrew psalm-settings, composed for Chichester Cathedral.

📖 *Season Highlights, pages 61 & 63*

This concert will be broadcast on BBC4

💬 **6.00pm Pre-Prom Talk** (RAH)
Sakari Oramo and Stephen Maddock on Ives's Symphony No. 4

PROM 12

Sunday 25 July
3.30pm – c5.30pm
Price Code **G**

NOTE TIME

Blue Peter Prom – Beating Drums, Dancing Lions

Liz Barker presenter
Simon Thomas presenter

Kagemusha Taiko drummers
Choy Lee Fut Kung Fu School

City of Birmingham Youth Chorus
BBC Philharmonic
Gianandrea Noseda conductor
Jason Lai conductor

See Prom 10 for details.

There will be one interval

Liz Barker and Simon Thomas

PROM 13

Sunday 25 July
7.30pm – c9.35pm
Price Code **A**

BBC4

Elgar
Violin Concerto in B minor   50'

interval

Dvořák
Mass in D major   42'

Rebecca Nash soprano
Louise Winter mezzo-soprano
Benjamin Hulett tenor
Neal Davies bass
Pinchas Zukerman violin

BBC Symphony Chorus
BBC Symphony Orchestra
Sir Andrew Davis conductor

The BBC Symphony Orchestra's Conductor Laureate returns for a pairing of two of this year's major anniversary composers. The great Pinchas Zukerman returns as the soloist in Elgar's glorious concerto (see also PCM 2). Originally composed with organ accompaniment, Dvořák's lyrical Mass is heard here in the orchestration that the composer himself made for its London premiere.

📖 *Back to Bohemia, pages 18–23; England at the Crossroads, pages 32–8*

This concert will be broadcast on BBC4

PROM 14

Monday 26 July
7.30pm – c9.55pm
Price Code **A**

BBC4

Taverner
In nomine*   3'

Sir Peter Maxwell Davies
First Fantasia on an 'In nomine' of John Taverner   11'

Beethoven
Piano Concerto No. 4 in G major   35'

interval

Elgar–Payne
Symphony No. 3   59'

Catherine Ennis organ*
Andreas Haefliger piano

BBC Scottish Symphony Orchestra
Martyn Brabbins conductor

The Proms celebrate the 70th birthday of the new Master of the Queen's Music with the revival of a 1962 BBC commission, preceded by the 16th-century organ work that inspired it. Also a BBC commission, Elgar's last symphony was famously left incomplete at his death in 1934, but successfully 'elaborated' from the surviving sketches by Anthony Payne and premiered by the BBC SO in 1998.

📖 *England at the Crossroads, pages 32–8; New Music, pages 46–52*

This concert will be broadcast on BBC4

🎵 **1.00pm Proms Chamber Music**
See pages 120–21

PROM 15

Tuesday 27 July
7.30pm – c9.35pm
Price Code **A**

BBC4

Dvořák
Czech Suite   23'

Saint-Saëns
Piano Concerto No. 2 in G minor 24'

interval

Schumann
Symphony No. 2 in C major   39'

Simon Trpčeski *piano*

Scottish Chamber Orchestra
Joseph Swensen *conductor*

Joseph Swensen

In our exploration of music from Bohemia, Dvořák's *Czech Suite* reworks traditional dance tunes from his native land. Schumann's uplifting and energetic Second Symphony is preceded by Saint-Saëns's radiant Second Piano Concerto, in which the Macedonian pianist Simon Trpčeski, a former BBC New Generation Artist, makes his Proms debut.

📖 *Back to Bohemia, pages 18–23*

This concert will be broadcast on BBC4

PROM 16

Wednesday 28 July
7.00pm – c9.00pm
Price Code **A**

 BBC4 NOTE TIME

Schubert
Symphony No. 8 in B minor,
'Unfinished'   25'

Janáček
Hukvaldy Songs*   15'

interval

Janáček
Glagolitic Mass   41'

Zdena Kloubová *soprano*
Karen Cargill *mezzo-soprano*
Pavol Breslik *tenor*
Gustáv Beláček *bass*
David Goode *organ*

Czech Philharmonic Chorus of Brno
London Philharmonic Orchestra
Kurt Masur *conductor*
Petr Fiala *conductor**

The London Philharmonic and Principal Conductor Kurt Masur are joined by a choir from anniversary composer Leoš Janáček's adopted home town for a performance of his blazing choral masterpiece, the *Glagolitic Mass*, preceded by his *a cappella* arrangements of folk songs from his Moravian birthplace.

📖 *Back to Bohemia, pages 18–23*

This concert will be broadcast on BBC4

💬 **5.30pm Pre-Prom Talk** (RCM)
Dennis Marks and Petr Fiala on Janáček's *Glagolitic Mass*

PROM 17

Wednesday 28 July
10.00pm – c11.20pm
Price Code **D**

 BBC rec LATE NIGHT

Britten
Curlew River   71'

Birmingham Opera Company

Mark Wilde *The Madwoman*
Rodney Clarke *The Ferryman*
Iain Paterson *The Traveller*
Keel Watson *The Abbot*
Birmingham Opera Company Chorus

Birmingham Contemporary Music Group
Graham Vick *stage director*

The influence of the East on Western music is nowhere more clearly felt than in the first of Britten's three 'church parables'. A unique fusion of ritualistic Oriental styles with Britten's innate sense of music theatre, *Curlew River* transposes a traditional Japanese Noh play to a monastic setting in the Norfolk fens and will here be given an 'in the round' staging within the Arena by Graham Vick, who has made a speciality of such 'walk-about' productions in his work with Birmingham Opera Company.

📖 *EAST/WEST, pages 4–12*

There will be no interval

This concert will be broadcast on BBC4

PROM 18

Thursday 29 July
7.30pm – c9.45pm
Price Code **A**

BBC4

Martinů
The Frescoes of Piero
della Francesca   19'

Mozart
Piano Concerto No. 23
in A major, K488   26'

interval

Mahler
Kindertotenlieder   26'

Janáček
Taras Bulba   23'

Alice Coote *mezzo-soprano*
Paul Lewis *piano*

BBC Symphony Orchestra
Sir Andrew Davis *conductor*

This season's Czech strand continues with the expatriate Martinů's evocation of 15th-century Italian frescoes seen in Arezzo and Janáček's rhapsody on Gogol's heroic tale about a Ukrainian Cossack freedom-fighter. In between, well-established former BBC New Generation Artists perform one of Mozart's sunniest concertos and one of Mahler's most intense song-cycles.

📖 *Back to Bohemia, pages 18–23*

This concert will be broadcast on BBC4

PROM 19

Friday 30 July
7.30pm – c9.30pm
Price Code **C**

Dvořák
Symphony No. 8 in G major   38'

interval

R. Strauss
Ein Heldenleben   44'

Bavarian Radio Symphony Orchestra
Mariss Jansons conductor

Mariss Jansons

The great Latvian conductor Mariss Jansons has provided some magnificent experiences for Proms audiences. He returns with the German radio orchestra of which he has recently become Chief Conductor. In the first of their two concerts, they perform anniversary composer Dvořák's pastoral Eighth Symphony and Strauss's autobiographical showpiece.

📖 *Back to Bohemia, pages 18–23*

This concert will be broadcast on BBC4

PROM 20

Saturday 31 July
7.00pm – c9.00pm
Price Code **C**

Shostakovich
Violin Concerto No. 1 in A minor   38'

interval

Tchaikovsky
Symphony No. 6 in B minor, 'Pathétique'   45'

Gidon Kremer violin

Bavarian Radio Symphony Orchestra
Mariss Jansons conductor

In their second – all-Russian – Prom, Mariss Jansons and his Bavarian orchestra are joined by charismatic leading violinist Gidon Kremer for one of the peaks of the 20th-century violin repertoire, paired with the tragic symphony whose premiere Tchaikovsky conducted just 10 days before his (possibly self-inflicted) death.

This concert will be broadcast on BBC2

PROM 21

Saturday 31 July
10.00pm – c11.45pm
Price Code **E**

'Out here to swing!'

Lincoln Center Jazz Orchestra
Wynton Marsalis trumpet/director

Wynton Marsalis

Multi-talented American trumpet virtuoso, educationalist and musical dynamo Wynton Marsalis is a regular visitor to the Proms and returns this year with his Lincoln Center Jazz Orchestra for a late-night celebration of the irresistible rhythms and roof-lifting riffs of the Golden Age of Swing.

There will be no interval

This concert will be broadcast on BBC4

PROM 22

Sunday 1 August
6.30pm – c8.10pm
Price Code **A**

Britten
Voluntary on Tallis's Lamentations   4'
world premiere

War Requiem   85'

Susan B. Anthony soprano
Ian Bostridge tenor
Simon Keenlyside baritone
Timothy Bond organ

Finchley Children's Music Group
London Symphony Chorus
London Symphony Orchestra
Sir Colin Davis conductor

It's 100 years since the LSO was formed by breakaway players from Henry Wood's Queen's Hall Orchestra. Earlier this year, Sir Colin Davis launched the LSO's centenary season with a performance of Britten's opera *Peter Grimes* and they now visit the Proms with another Britten masterpiece, his harrowing fusion of the Latin Mass for the Dead with the First World War poetry of Wilfred Owen. It is prefaced by the first performance of a recently-rediscovered organ work from the 1930s that uncannily anticipates the music of the *Requiem*'s Agnus Dei.

📖 *Season Highlights, page 64*

There will be no interval

💬 **5.00pm Pre-Prom Talk** (RCM)
Colin Matthews and Tommy Pearson on Britten's *War Requiem*

PROM 23 — Sunday 1 August
9.00pm – c11.55pm
Price Code **D**

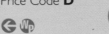

Sir John Tavener
The Veil of the Temple   c160'
world premiere of concert version

Patricia Rozario soprano
Simon Wall tenor
Andrew Rupp baritone
Thomas Guthrie baritone
Jeremy Birchall bass
Adrian Peacock bass

Dirk Campbell duduk
James Vivian organ

Holst Singers
The Choir of The Temple Church
Brighton Festival Chorus
Brass of the English Chamber Orchestra
Stephen Layton conductor

Sir John Tavener's all-night vigil made a deep impression when it was first heard at the Temple Church in London last summer. To celebrate his 60th birthday this year, the Proms present the premiere of a new concise concert version, brought to the Royal Albert Hall by many of the same musicians.

📖 *Season Highlights, page 65*

There will be no interval

PROM 24 — Monday 2 August
7.30pm – c9.40pm
Price Code **A**

Shostakovich
Overture on Russian and
Kirghiz Folk Themes   10'

Cage
The Seasons   16'

Tan Dun
Out of Peking Opera   17'

interval

Esa-Pekka Salonen
Laughing Unlearnt, for solo violin   11'
London premiere

Tan Dun
Concerto for water percussion
and orchestra (new version)   35'

Evelyn Glennie percussion
Cho-Liang Lin violin

BBC Symphony Orchestra
Tan Dun conductor

Tan Dun, the brilliant Oscar-winning Chinese-American composer of *Crouching Tiger, Hidden Dragon*, conducts two of his own concertos, an Eastern-influenced ballet by John Cage and an overture that Shostakovich wrote after visiting the Asian state of Kyrgyzstan.

📖 *EAST/WEST, pages 4–12;*
New Music, pages 46–52

🎵 **1.00pm Proms Chamber Music**
See pages 120–21

💬 **6.00pm Pre-Prom Talk** (RAH)
Tan Dun

PROM 25 — Tuesday 3 August
7.00pm – c9.15pm
Price Code **A**

Szymanowski
Concert Overture in E major,
Op. 12   12'

Britten
Violin Concerto   33'

Ravel
Tzigane   10'

interval

Dvořák
Symphony No. 6 in D major   45'

Maxim Vengerov violin

BBC Philharmonic
Vassily Sinaisky conductor

Maxim Vengerov returns to the Proms in Britten's Violin Concerto, composed in America in the dark months preceding the outbreak of the Second World War, and adds an encore in the form of Ravel's gypsy-inspired showpiece. Dvořák's effervescent Sixth was dubbed 'a Czech Christmas symphony' by the conductor Václav Talich. The concert opens with an overture by the young Szymanowski, based on a heroic poem by the Polish philosopher-poet Tadeusz Miciński, who was killed in the First World War after being mistaken for a Russian general.

📖 *Back to Bohemia, pages 18–23*

PROM 26 — Tuesday 3 August
10.00pm – c11.30pm
Price Code **D**

Zelenka
Overture a 7 in F major,
ZWV 188   23'

Biber
Battalia   9'

Zelenka
Concerto a 8 in G major,
ZWV 186   15'

Bach
Orchestral Suite No. 1 in C major,
BWV 1066   23'

Freiburg Baroque Orchestra
Gottfried von der Goltz conductor

Gottfried von der Goltz

One of Germany's leading period bands pairs Czech-born Heinrich Biber's famous 'Battle' sonata – a miniature 17th-century precursor of the *1812* – with music by his inventive younger compatriot, Jan Dismas Zelenka, who moved to Dresden, where music by his great contemporary J. S. Bach was heard.

📖 *Back to Bohemia, pages 18–23*

There will be no interval

PROM 27

Wednesday 4 August
7.30pm – c9.35pm
Price Code **A**

Sir Peter Maxwell Davies
Antarctic Symphony
(Symphony No. 8)*   41'

interval

Berlioz
Symphonie fantastique   50'

BBC Philharmonic
Sir Peter Maxwell Davies conductor*
Yan Pascal Tortelier conductor

Yan Pascal Tortelier

Sir Peter Maxwell Davies's Eighth Symphony, which he has said will be his last, was inspired by his sea voyage to the Antarctic. As part of our celebration of his 70th birthday, the composer himself conducts its first Proms performance. After the interval, the BBC Philharmonic's French-born Conductor Laureate unleashes Berlioz's phantasmagoric showpiece.

📖 *England at the Crossroads,*
pages 32–8

♪ **5.30pm Composer Portrait**
Sir Peter Maxwell Davies. See page 144

PROM 28

Thursday 5 August
7.30pm – c9.45pm
Price Code **B**

Anders Hillborg
Exquisite Corpse   17'
UK premiere

Sibelius
Violin Concerto in D minor   31'

interval

Songs by **Sibelius**, **Alfvén**
and **Stenhammar**   22'

Bartók
The Miraculous Mandarin – Suite 20'

Anne Sofie von Otter mezzo-soprano
Joshua Bell violin

Royal Stockholm Philharmonic Orchestra
Alan Gilbert conductor

The brilliant young American violinist Joshua Bell performs Sibelius's lyrical concerto. The Swedish mezzo Anne Sofie von Otter sings a selection of the Scandinavian songs she has made her own. The Royal Stockholm Philharmonic and its American Chief Conductor celebrate the 50th birthday of Swedish composer Anders Hillborg with his Surrealist-inspired 'collage'.

📖 *EAST/WEST, pages 4–12;*
New Music, pages 46–52

💬 **6.00pm Pre-Prom Talk** (RAH)
Anders Hillborg and Andrew Kurowski

PROM 29

Friday 6 August
7.00pm – c9.10pm
Price Code **A**

Takemitsu
Twill by Twilight   11'

Dvořák
Cello Concerto in B minor   41'

interval

Ravel
Shéhérazade – trois poèmes   17'

Respighi
The Pines of Rome   23'

Katarina Karnéus mezzo-soprano
Truls Mørk cello

BBC National Orchestra of Wales
Tadaaki Otaka conductor

The BBC's Welsh orchestra and its Japanese Conductor Laureate Tadaaki Otaka are joined by the Swedish mezzo-soprano Katarina Karnéus for Ravel's sensuous tribute to the mysterious Orient, offset by Japanese composer Tōru Takemitsu's typically Western-influenced homage to American composer Morton Feldman. Norwegian cellist Truls Mørk plays Dvořák's great concerto, premiered in London and full of nostalgia for the composer's Czech homeland. The concert ends with Respighi's sumptuous evocation of the sights and sounds of the Eternal City.

📖 *EAST/WEST, pages 4–12;*
Back to Bohemia, pages 18–23

PROM 30

Friday 6 August
10.00pm – c11.20pm
Price Code **D**

Anon (13th century)
Vetus abit littera   3'

Machaut
Messe de Nostre Dame   25'

Sir Harrison Birtwistle
Theseus Game*   37'

Hilliard Ensemble

London Sinfonietta*
Martyn Brabbins conductor*
Pierre-André Valade conductor*

The old meets the new in a programme that places the complexities of the earliest known single-composer setting of the Latin Mass alongside a recent work by Sir Harrison Birtwistle, who has long been influenced by early music, and whose 70th birthday we celebrate this year. Inspired by Greek myth, *Theseus Game* creates an orchestral maze for individual players to weave their way through, and is directed by the two conductors who gave the work its world premiere in Germany last September.

📖 *England at the Crossroads,*
pages 32–8

There will be no interval

PROM 31 — Saturday 7 August
7.00pm – c9.00pm
Price Code **A**

Smetana
Má vlast – Vyšehrad;
From Bohemia's Woods
and Fields; Vltava   36'

interval

Mahler
Symphony No. 1 in D major,
'Titan'   50'

**National Youth Orchestra
of Great Britain**
Sir Roger Norrington conductor

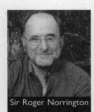
Sir Roger Norrington

The National Youth Orchestra of Great Britain pays its annual visit to the Proms under the inspirational conductor Sir Roger Norrington, who turned 70 earlier this year. The three most popular tone poems from Smetana's most proudly patriotic work, 'My Country', preface the titanic First Symphony of the Bohemian-born Mahler.

📖 *Back to Bohemia, pages 18–23*

This concert will be broadcast on BBC2

PROM 32 — Sunday 8 August
6.30pm – c8.45pm
Price Code **A**

Janáček
Sinfonietta   23'

interval

Dvořák
The Spectre's Bride
(sung in Czech)   80'

Eva Urbanová soprano
Peter Straka tenor
Ivan Kusnjer baritone

BBC Symphony Chorus
BBC Symphony Orchestra
Jiří Bělohlávek conductor

Janáček's magnificent *Sinfonietta* – sonic snapshots of famous landmarks in his adopted home town of Brno – opens this all-Czech programme in which the BBC Symphony Orchestra and Chorus are joined by their Czech-born former Principal Guest Conductor. Commissioned for the Birmingham Festival of 1885 (and later conducted by Janáček in Brno), Dvořák's once-popular, but now rarely-performed, oratorio retells a grisly legend of a love that reaches out from beyond the grave.

📖 *Back to Bohemia, pages 18–23*

💬 **5.00pm Pre-Prom Talk** (RAH)
Roderick Swanston on *The Spectre's Bride*

PROM 33 — Monday 9 August
7.00pm – c8.55pm
Price Code **A**

→

Ravel
Shéhérazade
– ouverture de féerie   15'

Messiaen
Poèmes pour Mi   28'

interval

Beethoven
Symphony No. 7 in A major   36'

Susan Bullock soprano

BBC Scottish Symphony Orchestra
Ilan Volkov conductor

Ilan Volkov

Following his successful Proms debut last season, Ilan Volkov returns with the orchestra of which he is Chief Conductor for a concert contrasting the heady perfume of Eastern-influenced French music – the 24-year-old Ravel's overture to an unwritten *Arabian Nights* opera and the 27-year-old Messiaen's set of nine love letters to his first wife – with the dancing athleticism of Beethoven's Seventh Symphony.

📖 *EAST/WEST, pages 4–12;*
Season Highlights, page 62

🎵 **1.00pm Proms Chamber Music**
See pages 120–21

PROM 34 — Monday 9 August
10.00pm – c11.30pm
Price Code **D**

← LATE NIGHT

Naji Hakim
Ouverture libanaise   10'

R. Strauss
Serenade in E flat major
for 13 wind instruments, Op. 7   9'

Messiaen
Messe de la Pentecôte –
Entrée (Les langues de feu);
Sortie (Le vent de l'Esprit)   5'

Offrande au Saint-Sacrement   5'

La Nativité du Seigneur
– Dieu parmi nous   8'

Dvořák
Serenade in D minor
for wind and strings   25'

Naji Hakim
In organo, chordis et choro   12'

Naji Hakim organ
London Winds
Michael Collins clarinet/director

Naji Hakim, Olivier Messiaen's successor as organist at La Trinité in Paris, plays two of his own works on the Royal Albert Hall's newly-restored organ, interspersed with sacred pieces by his great predecessor. Michael Collins and his ensemble pair the teenage Strauss's elegant wind serenade with Dvořák's lyrical highlight of the genre.

📖 *Season Highlights, page 62;*
Restored!, pages 94–6

There will be no interval

PROM 35

Tuesday 10 August
7.30pm – c9.40pm
Price Code **A**

Biber
Missa bruxellensis   50'

interval

Muffat
Armonico tributo –
Sonata V in G major   15'

Bach
Magnificat in D major, BWV 243   25'

Emma Kirkby *soprano*
Joanne Lunn *soprano*
Michael Chance *counter-tenor*
Matthew White *counter-tenor*
James Gilchrist *tenor*
Michael George *bass*

Academy of Ancient Music Chorus
Academy of Ancient Music
Paul Goodwin *conductor*

A spectacular polychoral experience.
Biber's Mass was written, near the end
of his life, for voices and instruments
dispersed around Salzburg Cathedral
and here marks the 300th anniversaries
of the Bohemian-born composer and of
his German colleague Georg Muffat,
whose *Armonico tributo* was a pioneering
collection of concerti grossi. Bach's
joyous *Magnificat* closes the concert.

📖 *Back to Bohemia, pages 18–23;
Proms Artists, pages 80–85*

💬 **6.00pm Pre-Prom Talk** (RAH)
The music of Heinrich Biber

PROM 36

Wednesday 11 August
7.30pm – c10.00pm
Price Code **A**

Mozart
Symphony No. 32 in G major,
K318   9'

Janáček
The Eternal Gospel
(sung in Czech)   22'

interval

Mahler
Symphony No. 7   80'

Gweneth-Ann Jeffers *soprano*
John Daszak *tenor*

London Philharmonic Choir
BBC Scottish Symphony Orchestra
Ilan Volkov *conductor*

A tiny opera-overture-cum-symphony
in Mozart's sunniest Italianate manner
and Mahler's darkly nocturnal Seventh
Symphony (premiered by him in Prague
in 1908) frame the first Proms
performance of *The Eternal Gospel*, a
visionary cantata about a kingdom of
the spirit governed by eternal love,
written by Janáček on the eve of the
First World War.

📖 *Back to Bohemia, pages 18–23*

💬 **6.00pm Pre-Prom Talk** (RAH)
Piers Burton-Page on Mahler's
Symphony No. 7

PROM 37

Thursday 12 August
7.30pm – c9.30pm
Price Code **A**

Lutoslawski
Mi-parti   15'

Szymanowski
Violin Concerto No. 2
in D major   22'

interval

Sibelius
Symphony No. 2 in D major   45'

Leonidas Kavakos *violin*

BBC Symphony Orchestra
Osmo Vänskä *conductor*

Osmo Vänskä

Osmo Vänskä
conducts the
BBC Symphony
Orchestra for the
first time at the
Proms in his fellow
Finn's nationalistic
Second Symphony.
The first half of the concert presents a
pair of 20th-century Polish classics:
Leonidas Kavakos is the soloist in
Szymanowski's Second Violin Concerto,
inspired by the 'savage, natural native
originality' of the folk music of the Tatra
Mountains, and Lutoslawski's luminous
Mi-parti is performed to mark the 10th
anniversary of its composer's death.

PROM 38

Friday 13 August
7.30pm – c9.45pm
Price Code **A**

Bright Sheng
The Song and Dance of Tears   26'
UK premiere

interval

Messiaen
Turangalîla Symphony   75'

Yo-Yo Ma *cello*
Wu Man *pipa*
Wu Tong *sheng/suona*
Joel Fan *piano*

Paul Crossley *piano*
Cynthia Millar *ondes martenot*

London Sinfonietta
David Robertson *conductor*

As a centrepiece of this season's EAST/
WEST theme, charismatic cellist Yo-Yo
Ma and colleagues from his Silk Road
Ensemble star in a new quadruple
concerto specially written for them
by Chinese-American composer
Bright Sheng. An expanded London
Sinfonietta continues our survey of
Messiaen's most monumental scores
with his erotically-charged, Eastern-
influenced *Turangalîla Symphony*.

📖 *EAST/WEST, pages 4–12;
Season Highlights, page 62;
Proms Artists, pages 80–85*

💬 **6.00pm Pre-Prom Talk** (RAH)
Bright Sheng and Gillian Moore

💬 **c10.00pm Proms Question
Time** (RAH) See page 144

PROM 39

Berlioz
Overture 'Le corsaire' 9'

Saint-Saëns
Symphony No. 3 in C minor,
'Organ' 35'

interval

Johann Strauss I
Radetzky March 3'

Johann Strauss II
Voices of Spring – waltz 7'

Johann Strauss I
Frederica – polka 3'

Cachucha-Galop 2'

Johann Strauss II
The Beautiful Blue Danube – waltz 10'

interspersed with operetta arias by
Kálmán, Zeller, Lehár
and **Stolz**

Yvonne Kenny *soprano*
Dame Gillian Weir *organ*

BBC Concert Orchestra
Barry Wordsworth *conductor*

Yvonne Kenny lends her voice to a Viennese selection celebrating the bicentenary of the birth of Johann Strauss the elder, and the BBC Concert Orchestra with its Principal Conductor are joined by Dame Gillian Weir to give the newly-restored Royal Albert Hall organ a workout in Saint-Saëns's 'Organ' Symphony, a work written for London.

📖 *Restored!, pages 94–6*

PROM 40

Music of the Silk Road

Programme to include:

Zhao Jiping
Moon Over Guan Mountain

Sandeep Das
Tarang

Kayhan Kalhor
Blue as the Turquoise Night of Neyshabur

Yo-Yo Ma *cello*
Silk Road Ensemble

In the second of their three Proms appearances to tie in with this season's EAST/WEST theme (*see also PCM 5*), Yo-Yo Ma and his Silk Road Ensemble explore yet more musical links between the Orient and the Occident. In a colourful and evocative programme including music and artists from China, India, Persia, Armenia and Kyrgyzstan, the extraordinary Indian *tabla* player Sandeep Das and Iranian spike-fiddle master Kayhan Kalhor feature in their own compositions, and Chinese *pipa* virtuoso Wu Man performs arrangements of Armenian folk songs and music of the Roma.

📖 *EAST/WEST, pages 4–12*

There will be one interval

PROM 41

Bach
Mass in B minor 110'

Katharine Fuge *soprano*
Renata Pokupić *soprano*
Sara Mingardo *mezzo-soprano*
Mark Padmore *tenor*
Dietrich Henschel *baritone*

Monteverdi Choir
English Baroque Soloists
Sir John Eliot Gardiner *conductor*

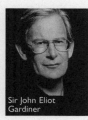
Sir John Eliot Gardiner

Following his millennial 'Bach Cantata Pilgrimage' in the year 2000, Sir John Eliot Gardiner returns to the Proms with his skilled teams of Baroque players and singers for a performance of Bach's monumental Mass, which combines the Leipzig Cantor's personal credo with a dazzling display of his compositional techniques.

📖 *Season Highlights, page 66*

There will be no interval

💬 **6.30pm Pre-Prom Talk** (RCM)
Sir John Eliot Gardiner on Bach's
B minor Mass

PROM 42

Musorgsky
Night on Bare Mountain 13'

Rimsky-Korsakov
Mlada – Act 3 37'

interval

Stravinsky
The Rite of Spring 33'

Mezzo-soprano and tenor soloists of the Kirov Opera

Apollo Voices
BBC Symphony Orchestra
Valery Gergiev *conductor*

Valery Gergiev conducts the BBC SO for the first time at the Proms in an all-Russian programme. Musorgsky's demonic tone poem foreshadows the witches' sabbath in Act 3 of his friend Rimsky-Korsakov's exotic opera-ballet *Mlada*, which in turn influenced the music of Rimsky's pupil, Stravinsky, whose father had sung in *Mlada*'s premiere.

📖 *Season Highlights, page 61*

This concert will be broadcast on BBC1

🎵 **1.00pm Proms Chamber Music**
See pages 120–21

💬 **6.00pm Pre-Prom Talk** (RAH)
David Nice on *Mlada*

PROM 43

Tuesday 17 August
7.30pm – c9.35pm
Price Code **B**

Brahms
Symphony No. 3 in F major   33'

interval

Sir Harrison Birtwistle
Four Settings of Alfred Brendel   c14'
BBC commission: world premiere

Beethoven
Piano Concerto No. 5 in E flat major,
'Emperor'   39'

William Dazeley *baritone*
Alfred Brendel *piano*

Philharmonia Orchestra
Christoph von Dohnányi *conductor*

Alfred Brendel, one of the greatest
artists of our age, makes his last Proms
appearance before retiring from live
broadcasts. His farewell performance
of Beethoven's majestic final piano
concerto is preceded by new settings
of Brendel's own poetry by his close
friend Sir Harrison Birtwistle.

📖 *England at the Crossroads,*
pages 32–8; New Music, pages 46–52;
Proms Artists, pages 80–85

🎵 **6.00pm Composer Portrait**
Sir Harrison Birtwistle. *See page 144*

PROM 44

Wednesday 18 August
7.30pm – c9.40pm
Price Code **A**

Hans Werner Henze
Symphony No. 10   42'
UK premiere

interval

Mozart
Piano Concerto No. 20
in D minor, K466   30'

R. Strauss
Don Juan   17'

Richard Goode *piano*

Hamburg Philharmonic Orchestra
Ingo Metzmacher *conductor*

Ingo Metzmacher, who made his Proms
conducting debut with the acclaimed
UK premiere of Henze's Ninth
Symphony in 2000, returns with the
orchestra of which he is Music Director
to introduce Henze's rhapsodic Tenth
Symphony to this country. Richard
Goode is the soloist in Mozart's
turbulent D minor Piano Concerto, and
the concert closes with Strauss's
swaggering portrait of Don Juan.

📖 *New Music, pages 46–52*

💬 **6.00pm Pre-Prom Talk** (RCM)
Malcolm MacDonald on Henze's
Symphony No. 10

PROM 45

Thursday 19 August
7.00pm – c9.40pm
Price Code **C**

Wagner
Das Rheingold (concert
performance; sung in German)   150'

Willard W. White *Wotan*
Kim Begley *Loge*
James Rutherford *Donner*
Timothy Robinson *Froh*
Yvonne Naef *Fricka*
Geraldine McGreevy *Freia*
Anna Larsson *Erda*
Oleg Bryjak *Alberich*
Robin Leggate *Mime*
Peter Rose *Fasolt*
Robert Lloyd *Fafner*
Kate Royal *Woglinde*
Karen England *Wellgunde*
Christine Rice *Flosshilde*

**Orchestra of the Age of
Enlightenment**
Sir Simon Rattle *conductor*

Sir Simon Rattle and the OAE launch
the first ever *Ring* cycle at the Proms –
to be shared between different teams
of performers over the next four years
– with the first modern performance of
a Wagner opera on period instruments.

📖 *Season Highlights, page 67;*
Proms Artists, pages 80–85

There will be no interval

🎵 **4.45pm Pre-Prom Event** (RCA)
OAE/Camden schools *Rheingold* project

💬 **5.30pm Pre-Prom Talk** (RAH)
John Deathridge on Wagner's *Rheingold*

PROM 46

Friday 20 August
7.00pm – c9.25pm
Price Code **A**

Humperdinck
Hansel and Gretel (concert
performance; sung in German)   107'

Jennifer Larmore *Hansel*
Rebecca Evans *Gretel*
Elizabeth Connell *Mother*
Alan Opie *Father*
Jane Henschel *Witch*
Gillian Keith *Dew Fairy*
Mary Nelson *Sandman*

**London Oratory School
Chamber Choir**
BBC Concert Orchestra
Jane Glover *conductor*

Jane Glover

One of the most
successful operas
ever written for a
family audience,
this entrancing tale
of threatened
innocence and
vanquished evil has
many lessons for today. A 'child-friendly'
mix of folk melodies and Wagnerian
technique, it is revived to mark its
composer's 150th anniversary.

📖 *Season Highlights, page 68*

There will be one interval

💬 **5.30pm Pre-Prom Talk** (RAH)
Mark Lowther on *Hansel and Gretel*

PROM 47

Saturday 21 August
7.00pm – c9.00pm
Price Code **A**

Handel
Coronation anthem
'My Heart is Inditing'   12'

Arne
Artaxerxes – three arias*   13'

Bach
Concerto in D minor
for two violins, BWV 1043   13'

interval

Rebel
Les élémens – Le cahos   7'

Vivaldi
Gloria in D major, RV 589   29'

Emma Bell *soprano**
Ailish Tynan *soprano*
Catherine Wyn-Rogers
mezzo-soprano
Rachel Podger *violin*

The English Concert
Choir of The English Concert
Andrew Manze *violin/conductor*

Vivaldi's exuberant *Gloria* is the climax of a concert of Baroque gems including one of Handel's anthems for the Coronation of George II, three arias from an opera about ancient Persia by the composer of *Rule, Britannia!*, Bach's popular Double Concerto and Jean-Féry Rebel's astonishing depiction of chaos.

This concert will be broadcast on BBC2

PROM 48

Saturday 21 August
10.00pm – c11.25pm
Price Code **D**

Janáček
Our Father *(sung in Czech)*   15'

Mark-Anthony Turnage
Calmo   3'
BBC commission: world premiere

James MacMillan
Le tombeau de Georges Rouault   14'

Holst
Choral Hymns from the Rig Veda –
Group 3   13'

Petr Eben
Sunday Music – Moto ostinato   5'

Judith Bingham
The Secret Garden   c20'
BBC commission: world premiere

Thomas Walker *tenor*
Sioned Williams *harp*
Thomas Trotter *organ*

BBC Symphony Chorus
Stephen Jackson *conductor*

The BBC Symphony Chorus premieres new works by British composers, alongside settings of the Lord's Prayer and Hindu hymns by anniversary composers Janáček and Holst. Birmingham's City Organist plays a solo work specially written for him by James MacMillan and another by the Czech Republic's foremost composer for organ.

EAST/WEST, pages 4–12; Back to Bohemia, pages 18–23; New Music, pages 46–52; Restored!, pages 94–6

There will be no interval

PROM 49

Sunday 22 August
6.30pm – c8.30pm
Price Code **A**

Ravel, orch. Grainger
Miroirs – La vallée des cloches   6'

McPhee
Tabuh-tabuhan   20'

Ives, arr. John Adams
Songs of Ragtime
and Reminiscence   15'
UK premiere

interval

John Adams
Doctor Atomic – Easter Eve 1945 12'
UK premiere

The Dharma at Big Sur   23'
UK premiere

Audra McDonald *soprano*
Tracy Silverman *electric violin*

BBC Symphony Orchestra
John Adams *conductor*

New works by John Adams, including a sneak preview of his next opera and song arrangements sung by 2002 Last Night star Audra McDonald, are prefaced by Percy Grainger's extraordinary orchestration of a piano piece by Ravel and Colin McPhee's exuberant re-creation of Balinese gamelan music.

EAST/WEST, pages 4–12; New Music, pages 46–52; Season Highlights, page 63

💬 **5.00pm Pre-Prom Talk** (RAH)
John Adams

PROM 50

Monday 23 August
7.00pm – c9.05pm
Price Code **B**

Glinka
Valse-Fantaisie in B minor   9'

Prokofiev
Piano Concerto No. 2 in G minor 32'

interval

Tchaikovsky
Symphony No. 5 in E minor   50'

Yefim Bronfman *piano*

St Petersburg Philharmonic
Yuri Temirkanov *conductor*

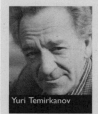

Yuri Temirkanov

The St Petersburg Philharmonic and its Chief Conductor Yuri Temirkanov have won huge acclaim on their recent visits to London; they return to present the first of two all-Russian concerts featuring the music of Glinka – the 'father of Russian opera' – in his bicentenary year. Tchaikovsky's Fifth Symphony is among his most impassioned and intense works. Yefim Bronfman is the soloist in Prokofiev's demanding and brilliant Second Piano Concerto.

♪ **1.00pm Proms Chamber Music**
See pages 120–21

PROM 51

Monday 23 August
10.00pm – c11.30pm
Price Code **E**

Kraus
Symphony in C major, VB 138 · 13'

Folke Rabe
Sardine Sarcophagus · 17'

HK Gruber
Three MOB Pieces · 11'

Beethoven
Symphony No. 4 in B flat major · 30'

Håkan Hardenberger trumpet

Swedish Chamber Orchestra
Thomas Dausgaard conductor

Håkan Hardenberger

Brilliant Swedish trumpeter Håkan Hardenberger is the soloist in two off-the-wall works: maverick Viennese composer HK Gruber's *Three MOB Pieces* and fellow Swede Folke Rabe's intriguingly-entitled *Sardine Sarcophagus*, which was commissioned for first performance in a converted sardine factory and pays tribute to the music of Mahler, *Das Lied von der Erde* in particular. The concert opens with a symphony by a Swedish contemporary of Mozart, and closes with Beethoven's punchy Fourth.

There will be no interval

PROM 52

Tuesday 24 August
7.30pm – c9.20pm
Price Code **B**

Glinka
Ruslan and Lyudmila – dances · 16'

Musorgsky
Songs and Dances of Death · 20'

interval

Rakhmaninov
Symphonic Dances · 35'

Dmitri Hvorostovsky baritone

St Petersburg Philharmonic
Yuri Temirkanov conductor

The St Petersburg Philharmonic and Yuri Temirkanov continue their celebration of Glinka's bicentenary with dances from the fantastical opera that has proved perhaps the most influential score in all Russian music. The great Russian baritone Dmitri Hvorostovsky sings Musorgsky's morbidly spine-tingling song-cycle. And the concert ends with Rakhmaninov's orchestral swansong – three movements which, the composer once said, run their course from midday to midnight.

📖 *Proms Artists, pages 80–85*

PROM 53

Wednesday 25 August
7.00pm – c9.15pm
Price Code **A**

NOTE TIME

Dvořák
Serenade in E major for strings · 27'

Schumann
Piano Concerto in A minor · 30'

interval

Chopin
Piano Concerto No. 2 in F minor · 32'

Dvořák
Slavonic Dance in E minor,
Op. 72 No. 2 · 5'

Legend in G minor, Op. 59 No. 3 · 4'

Lausanne Chamber Orchestra
Christian Zacharias piano/conductor

Christian Zacharias

Two of the greatest piano concertos in the repertory come together in the Lausanne Chamber Orchestra's Proms debut, featuring its Indian-born Music Director Christian Zacharias as soloist and director. Our anniversary survey of the music of Dvořák continues with his serene String Serenade and two orchestrations of Slavonic miniatures originally composed for piano duet.

📖 *Back to Bohemia, pages 18–23*

PROM 54

Wednesday 25 August
10.00pm – c11.20pm
Price Code **D**

LATE NIGHT

Britten
Sinfonietta · 15'

Lambert
Eight Poems of Li-Po* · 13'

Holst
Sāvitri · 35'

Sarah Connolly *Sāvitri*
John Mark Ainsley tenor*/*Satyavan*
Christopher Maltman *Death*

London Voices
Nash Ensemble
Martyn Brabbins conductor

Britten's Sinfonietta is a precociously early work (his official Op. 1), premiered in London in 1933, a year before the death of anniversary composer Gustav Holst, whose intimate chamber opera *Sāvitri* – about a wife who saves her dying husband's life – is imbued with the composer's deep love of Indian literature and philosophy. Constant Lambert's miniature settings of Chinese verse were inspired by his passion for screen actress Anna May Wong.

📖 *EAST/WEST, pages 4–12; England at the Crossroads, pages 32–8*

There will be no interval

PROM 55

Thursday 26 August
7.30pm – c10.00pm
Price Code **B**

PROM 56

Friday 27 August
7.30pm – c9.55pm
Price Code **A**

PROM 57

Saturday 28 August
6.30pm – c8.40pm
Price Code **B**

PROM 55

Glyndebourne Festival Opera

Rakhmaninov
The Miserly Knight
(semi-staged; sung in Russian)   60'

Sergei Leiferkus Old Baron
Richard Berkeley-Steele Albert
Albert Schagidullin Duke
Viateschlav Voinarovski Salomon
Maxim Mikhailov Servant

interval

Vladimir Jurowski

Puccini
Gianni Schicchi
(semi-staged; sung in Italian)   55'

Alessandro Corbelli Gianni Schicchi
Sally Matthews Lauretta
Massimo Giordano Rinuccio
Olga Schalaewa Nella
Marie McLaughlin La Ciesca
Felicity Palmer Zita
Adrian Thompson Gherardo
Eric Roberts Ser Amantio di Nicolao
Maxim Mikhailov Betto di Signa
Luigi Roni Simone
Viateschlav Voinarovski Maestro
Spinelloccio
James Gower Pinellino
Robert Davies Guccio

London Philharmonic Orchestra
Vladimir Jurowski conductor

Glyndebourne Festival Opera makes its annual visit to the Proms with its new double-bill of early-20th-century operas inspired by the root of all evil. *The Miserly Knight*, Rakhmaninov's rarely-performed setting of a play by Pushkin, was written for the great Russian bass Chaliapin, though he never actually sang it on stage. *Gianni Schicchi*, Puccini's quicksilver comedy (incongruously based on Dante's *Inferno*), was unveiled at New York's Metropolitan Opera in 1918 and contains some of his wittiest music; its most famous aria, 'O mio babbino caro', falls to BBC New Generation Artist Sally Matthews.

Season Highlights, pages 69 & 70; Proms Artists, pages 80–85

💬 **6.00pm Pre-Prom Talk** (RAH)
Nicholas Payne

PROM 56

Hindemith
Concert Music for Brass
and Strings   17'

Wagner, orch. Mottl
Wesendonck-Lieder   21'

Wagner
Tristan und Isolde –
Prelude and Liebestod   17'

interval

Beethoven
Symphony No. 3 in E flat major,
'Eroica'   50'

Deborah Voigt soprano

Royal Philharmonic Orchestra
Daniele Gatti conductor

Deborah Voigt

After a much-praised complete Beethoven cycle in London last year, the Royal Philharmonic Orchestra and Music Director Daniele Gatti bring the heroic Third Symphony to the Proms. Leading Wagnerian soprano Deborah Voigt performs the climactic *Liebestod* from the composer's *Tristan und Isolde*, prefaced by the radiant songs Wagner composed partly as preliminary studies for the opera.

PROM 57

Berio
Stanze*   30'

interval

Mahler
Das Lied von der Erde   65'

Andreas Schmidt baritone*
Yvonne Naef mezzo-soprano
Anthony Dean Griffey tenor

London Voices (men's voices)
Orchestre de Paris
Christoph Eschenbach conductor

The last work of the Italian composer Luciano Berio, completed just two weeks before his death last year, *Stanze* is a setting of verses by various poets – including Alfred Brendel – scored for solo baritone, three men's choruses and orchestra. A quasi-symphonic setting of ancient Chinese poems (in German translation) which reveals the direct influence of the Chinese music that Mahler had heard, *The Song of the Earth* culminates in possibly the most achingly extended leave-taking in all Western music.

EAST/WEST, pages 4–12; Proms Extras, pages 142–3

This concert will be broadcast on BBC2

💬 **5.00pm Pre-Prom Talk** (RAH)
David Osmond-Smith on Berio

PROM 58

Sunday 29 August
6.30pm – c8.30pm
Price Code **A**

Enescu
Romanian Rhapsody No. 1
in A major   12'

Bartók
Viola Concerto   21'

interval

Debussy, orch. Koechlin
Khamma   20'

Lutoslawski
Concerto for Orchestra   29'

Yuri Bashmet viola

BBC Symphony Orchestra
Jukka-Pekka Saraste conductor

The Proms debut of Debussy's rarely-heard Egyptian ballet *Khamma* is framed by a trio of folk-influenced scores from Eastern Europe. The Romanian composer George Enescu's gypsy-style rhapsody remains perhaps his most popular work. Béla Bartók's Viola Concerto, left unfinished at his death, ends in a burst of foot-stamping Hungarian dance rhythms. Witold Lutoslawski's modern orchestral classic, revived for the 10th anniversary of his death, offers an exuberantly mid-20th-century take on traditional Polish idioms.

📖 *EAST/WEST, pages 4–12; Proms Artists, pages 80–85*

PROM 59

Monday 30 August
3.30pm – c5.35pm
Price Code **A**

Brahms
Piano Concerto No. 1
in D minor   44'

interval

Carl Vine
Celebrare celeberrime   6'
UK premiere

Shostakovich
Symphony No. 1 in F minor   35'

Hélène Grimaud piano

Australian Youth Orchestra
Lawrence Foster conductor

Lawrence Foster

In a special Bank Holiday matinee concert, Lawrence Foster and the Australian Youth Orchestra perform Shostakovich's youthful First Symphony and Brahms's monumental First Piano Concerto with the free-spirited French pianist Hélène Grimaud. A celebratory work from Carl Vine marks the Australian composer's 50th birthday.

📖 *Proms Artists, pages 80–85*

🎵 **1.00pm Proms Chamber Music**
See pages 120–21

PROM 60

Monday 30 August
7.30pm – c9.45pm
Price Code **C**

Debussy
Prélude à L'après-midi d'un faune   10'

André Previn
Violin Concerto   38'

interval

Prokofiev
Symphony No. 5 in B flat major   46'

Anne-Sophie Mutter violin

Oslo Philharmonic Orchestra
André Previn conductor

Anne-Sophie Mutter

André Previn makes a long-awaited return to the Proms with the Norwegian orchestra of which he became Music Director last season, and with the violin concerto that he recently wrote especially for his wife, Anne-Sophie Mutter. Debussy's languidly erotic reverie was turned into a notorious *succès de scandale* when choreographed by Nijinsky for Diaghilev's Ballets Russes. And the concert ends with Prokofiev's rousingly popular Fifth Symphony.

📖 *Season Highlights, page 61*

PROM 61

Tuesday 31 August
7.30pm – c9.15pm
Price Code **A**

Monteverdi
Vespers of 1610   95'

Carolyn Sampson soprano
Rebecca Outram soprano
Charles Humphries counter-tenor
Charles Daniels tenor
James Gilchrist tenor
Daniel Auchincloss tenor
Nicholas Mulroy tenor
Matthew Vine tenor
Robert Evans bass
Robert Macdonald bass

Choir of The King's Consort
The King's Consort
Robert King director

Robert King and The King's Consort are currently recording Monteverdi's complete sacred music. They bring to the Proms his magnificent *Vespers of 1610* – one of the high points of the early Baroque period and a work whose opulent sonorities will swell to fill the unique spaces of the Royal Albert Hall.

📖 *Season Highlights, page 71*

There will be no interval

💬 **6.00pm Pre-Prom Talk** (RAH)
Robert King

PROM 62	PROM 63	PROM 64	PROM 65
Wednesday 1 September	Thursday 2 September	Friday 3 September	Friday 3 September
7.30pm – c9.45pm	7.00pm – c9.05pm	7.00pm – c9.10pm	10.00pm – c11.45pm
Price Code **A**	Price Code **A**	Price Code **C**	Price Code **E**

PROM 62

Britten
The Prince of the Pagodas
– excerpt   c20'

John Corigliano
Clarinet Concerto   29'
London premiere

interval

Musorgsky, orch. various
Pictures at an Exhibition   c50'
*introduced from the stage
by Leonard Slatkin*

Michael Collins clarinet

BBC Symphony Chorus
(men's voices)
BBC Symphony Orchestra
Leonard Slatkin conductor

Michael Collins

Leonard Slatkin celebrates his 60th birthday with a concert featuring the gamelan-inspired sounds of Britten's exotic ballet *The Prince of the Pagodas*, American composer John Corigliano's festive Clarinet Concerto, and Slatkin's own guided tour through lesser-known orchestrations of Musorgsky's famous picture gallery.

📖 *EAST/WEST, pages 4–12*

💬 **6.00pm Pre-Prom Talk** (RAH)
John Corigliano and John Allison

PROM 63

Joby Talbot
Sneaker Wave   c13'
BBC commission: world premiere

Weill
Songs – to include selection
from *Lady in the Dark*   c25'

interval

Alun Hoddinott
Euphonium Concerto   20'
London premiere

Shostakovich
Symphony No. 9 in E flat major   27'

Ruthie Henshall singer
David Childs euphonium

BBC National Orchestra of Wales
Grant Llewellyn conductor

Best known for his collaborations with The Divine Comedy, Joby Talbot is increasingly busy as an orchestral composer; his new work was inspired by the waves on a Californian beach. We mark the 75th birthday of Alun Hoddinott with the concerto he wrote for the young euphonium virtuoso David Childs. West End and Proms in the Park star Ruthie Henshall sings Broadway songs by Kurt Weill.

📖 *New Music, pages 46–52*

💬 **5.30pm Pre-Prom Talk** (RAH)
Joby Talbot and Mark Russell

PROM 64

Mozart
Symphony No. 41 in C major,
K551 'Jupiter'   35'

interval

Bruckner
Symphony No. 7 in E major   67'

Dresden Staatskapelle
Bernard Haitink conductor

Bernard Haitink

Bernard Haitink, Chief Conductor of the Dresden Staatskapelle, celebrated his 75th birthday earlier this year with the start of a series in which he will conduct several of the world's leading orchestras. In the first of his two Proms with the world's oldest orchestra, he conducts Mozart's final symphony and Bruckner's solemn memorial tribute to his musical hero, Richard Wagner, who was himself music director of the Staatskapelle in the 1840s.

PROM 65

Pierre Boulez
Sur Incises   40'

Stravinsky
Four Russian Peasant Songs
(a cappella version)   5'

Les noces   24'

Catrin Wyn-Davies soprano
Hilary Summers mezzo-soprano
Toby Spence tenor
Tigran Martirossian bass

BBC Singers
Ensemble Intercontemporain
Pierre Boulez conductor

Pierre Boulez conducts IRCAM's resident new music ensemble in his first Late Night Prom in the Royal Albert Hall. His own dazzling *Sur Incises* – for three pianists, three harpists and three percussionists (playing bells, marimbas, vibraphones and steel drums) – won the coveted Grawemeyer Award in 2000. Our anniversary survey of ballet scores commissioned by Diaghilev continues with *Les noces*, Stravinsky's percussive evocation of Russian wedding rituals, here prefaced by the related set of peasant songs, performed *a cappella* by the BBC Singers.

📖 *Season Highlights, page 61*

There will be no interval

PROM 66
Saturday 4 September
7.00pm – c9.00pm
Price Code **C**

 NOTE TIME

Haydn
Symphony No. 86 in D major   26'

Bartók
Dance Suite   17'

interval

Dvořák
Symphony No. 7 in D minor   35'

Dresden Staatskapelle
Bernard Haitink *conductor*

In the second of their two Proms, Bernard Haitink and the Dresden Staatskapelle perform one of Haydn's 'Paris' symphonies, a work composed by Bartók to mark the 50th anniversary of the founding of Budapest, and Dvořák's darkly dramatic Seventh Symphony, commissioned by the Royal Philharmonic Society on his first visit to Britain, in 1884, and premiered in London the following year, with the composer himself conducting.

📖 *Back to Bohemia, pages 18–23*

This concert will be broadcast on BBC2

PROM 67
Sunday 5 September
6.30pm – c8.35pm
Price Code **C**

NOTE TIME

Schoenberg
Variations for Orchestra, Op. 31   23'

interval

Beethoven
Symphony No. 9 in D minor, 'Choral'   70'

Christiane Oelze *soprano*
Birgit Remmert *mezzo-soprano*
Jonas Kaufmann *tenor*
John Relyea *bass*

City of Birmingham Symphony Chorus
Berliner Philharmoniker
Sir Simon Rattle *conductor*

Sir Simon Rattle

Sir Simon Rattle brings together his great Berlin orchestra and his former Birmingham choir for the annual Proms performance of Beethoven's life-affirming Ninth Symphony (with its famous burst of 'Turkish' music in the choral finale), prefaced by a work that the Berlin Philharmonic premiered back in 1928: Schoenberg's landmark set of 12-tone variations on the name of Bach.

📖 *EAST/WEST, pages 4–12*

This concert will be broadcast on BBC4

PROM 68
Monday 6 September
7.30pm – c9.30pm
Price Code **C**

Debussy
La mer   24'

interval

Messiaen
Éclairs sur l'Au-delà …   62'

Berliner Philharmoniker
Sir Simon Rattle *conductor*

In their second Prom, Sir Simon Rattle and his Berlin players perform the impressionistic sea symphony which Debussy completed in Eastbourne, and conclude our survey of Messiaen's music with his last major orchestral work, a visionary glimpse into a world beyond death.

📖 *Season Highlights, page 62*

This concert will be broadcast on BBC4

🎵 **1.00pm Proms Chamber Music**
See pages 120–21

💬 **5.45pm Audience Forum** (RAH)
Nicholas Kenyon and David Elliott

PROM 69
Tuesday 7 September
7.30pm – c9.35pm
Price Code **A**

Kaija Saariaho
Orion   25'
UK premiere

interval

Bartók
Duke Bluebeard's Castle   63'

Ildikó Komlósi *mezzo-soprano*
László Polgár *bass*

BBC Symphony Orchestra
Jukka-Pekka Saraste *conductor*

Jukka-Pekka Saraste

Finnish 'spectralist' Kaija Saariaho's beautifully crystalline depiction of Orion, the constellation, mythical hunter and demigod, prefaces Béla Bartók's only opera, a disturbing exposé of the dark secrets in Duke Bluebeard's past.

📖 *New Music, pages 46–52*

This concert will be broadcast on BBC4

💬 **6.00pm Pre-Prom Talk** (RAH)
Kaija Saariaho and Tom Service

PROM 70

Wednesday 8 September
7.00pm – c9.05pm
Price Code **B**

  BBC4 NOTE TIME

Dvořák
Scherzo capriccioso _13'_

Violin Concerto in A minor _31'_

interval

Dvořák
Symphony No. 9 in E minor, 'From the New World' _42'_

Sarah Chang violin

Czech Philharmonic Orchestra
Sir Charles Mackerras conductor

On the day of Dvořák's birthday, Sir Charles Mackerras, our leading champion of Czech music for the past five decades, conducts the Czech Philharmonic Orchestra, of which he is Principal Guest Conductor, in the vibrant _Scherzo capriccioso_, the richly lyrical Violin Concerto and the ever-popular 'New World' Symphony, which Dvořák himself conducted in the orchestra's inaugural concert in January 1896.

📖 _Back to Bohemia, pages 18–23_

This concert will be broadcast on BBC4

🔊 **5.30pm Pre-Prom Talk** (RCM)
Stephanie Hughes and members of the Czech Philharmonic Orchestra

PROM 71

Wednesday 8 September
10.00pm – c11.25pm
Price Code **D**

 LATE NIGHT

Sir Peter Maxwell Davies
Fantasia and a Ground on Two Pavans, after Purcell _6'_

Missa super L'homme armé _22'_

Stravinsky
Ragtime _5'_

Sir Peter Maxwell Davies
Linguae ignis _13'_

Stravinsky
Renard _17'_

Psappha
Nicholas Kok conductor

Nicholas Kok

The Manchester-based chamber ensemble Psappha makes its Proms debut in a concert marking the exact 70th birthday of Mancunian composer Sir Peter Maxwell Davies. Two works from the 1960s are contrasted with the pentecostal _Linguae ignis_, composed just two years ago. _Renard_, Stravinsky's foxy farmyard burlesque, rounds off our 75th-anniversary survey of music commissioned by Diaghilev.

📖 _England at the Crossroads, pages 32–8; Season Highlights, page 61_

There will be no interval

PROM 72

Thursday 9 September
7.30pm – c9.45pm
Price Code **A**

BBC4

Charpentier
Requiem (Messe pour les trépassés) _56'_

interval

Charpentier
Messe pour plusieurs instruments au lieu des orgues _20'_

Te Deum _23'_

Jaël Azzaretti soprano
Olga Pitarch soprano
Paul Agnew tenor
Jeffrey Thompson tenor
Topi Lehtipuu tenor
Marc Mauillon tenor
João Fernandes bass
Bertrand Bontoux bass

Choir and Orchestra of Les Arts Florissants
William Christie conductor

entente cordiale

Les Arts Florissants and William Christie present a concert of sacred music to mark the 300th anniversary of the great French composer from one of whose operas the ensemble took its name. Presented as part of this year's Anglo-French celebration of the Entente Cordiale.

📖 _Season Highlights, page 72_

This concert will be broadcast on BBC4

🔊 **6.00pm Pre-Prom Talk** (RAH)
William Christie and Edward Blakeman

PROM 73

Friday 10 September
7.30pm – c9.50pm
Price Code **A**

BBC4

Dvořák
The Water Goblin _14'_

Rusalka – Song to the Moon _5'_

Puccini
La bohème – Musetta's Waltz Song _3'_

Manon Lescaut – Intermezzo _7'_

Bellini
I puritani – Mad scene _18'_

interval

Shostakovich
Symphony No. 5 in D minor _50'_

Anna Netrebko soprano

BBC Philharmonic
Gianandrea Noseda conductor

The Russian soprano Anna Netrebko recently scored major successes on stage and on disc with Gianandrea Noseda, and here joins him and the BBC Philharmonic in a selection of arias and scenes from Italian and Czech opera, including the radiant 'Song to the Moon' from anniversary composer Antonín Dvořák's _Rusalka_. Shostakovich's Fifth Symphony, premiered at the height of Stalin's Terror and originally dubbed 'a Soviet artist's creative reply to just criticism', remains his most popular, if powerfully ambiguous, work.

📖 _Back to Bohemia, pages 18–23_

This concert will be broadcast on BBC4

PROM 74

Saturday 11 September
7.30pm – c10.30pm
Price Code **F**

THE LAST NIGHT OF THE PROMS 2004

Dvořák Overture 'Carnival'	10'	**Sousa** Liberty Bell – march	5'	
R. Strauss Horn Concerto No. 1 in E flat major	16'	**Elgar** Pomp and Circumstance March No. 1	8'	
Vaughan Williams Five Mystical Songs	19'	**Wood**, arr. John Wilson & Stephen Jackson Fantasia on British Sea-Songs	23'	
Barber Toccata festiva	12'	**Parry**, orch. Elgar Jerusalem	2'	
interval		The National Anthem	2'	
Sir Peter Maxwell Davies Ojai Festival Overture	6'	Auld Lang Syne	1'	
Puccini Madam Butterfly – Humming Chorus	3'			
Rodgers & Hammerstein Oklahoma! – 'O what a beautiful morning'	3'			
Cole Porter Kiss Me, Kate – 'Where is the life that late I led?'	5'			
Gilbert & Sullivan The Mikado – 'I've got a little list'	2'			

Sir Thomas Allen *baritone*
Simon Preston *organ*
David Pyatt *horn*

BBC Singers
BBC Symphony Chorus
BBC Symphony Orchestra
Leonard Slatkin *conductor*

The celebrations of the Last Night range from the anniversaries of Dvořák and Peter Maxwell Davies to echoes of our Eastern theme in Puccini's chorus and Sullivan's 'list' song, and the Royal Albert Hall organ at full throttle in Samuel Barber's festive toccata. Our soloists include one of Britain's most distinguished singers in Vaughan Williams and musical comedy, and a graduate of the BBC Young Musician competition in an extrovert concerto that Richard Strauss wrote for his father. The four nations of the UK once again join in for the rousing finale.

📖 *EAST/WEST, pages 4–12; Back to Bohemia, pages 18–23; England at the Crossroads, pages 32–8; Restored!, pages 94–6*

This concert will be broadcast on BBC2 (Part 1) and BBC1 (Part 2)

PROMS
in the Park

The BBC presents the ninth season of Proms in the Park, bringing the atmosphere of the Last Night of the Proms simultaneously to audiences in London, Manchester, Belfast, Glasgow and Swansea. All five Proms in the Park events will culminate in live big-screen link-ups with the Royal Albert Hall.

BBC Proms in the Park continues to be a colourful conclusion to the season's programme, attracting capacity audiences to outdoor venues across the country, with all events sponsored by Renault. This year's concerts are broadcast live across BBC Radio and Television: BBC Radio 2 broadcasts from Hyde Park, and BBC Radio Ulster, BBC Radio Scotland, BBC Radio Wales and GMR broadcast their local events. Highlights of all five Proms in the Park will be included as part of the coverage of the Last Night on BBC1 and BBC2, while Digital TV viewers can swap between the Royal Albert Hall and the Proms in the Park events across the UK.

Events sponsored by
RENAULT

BBC Proms in the Park, London

Dynamic percussionist Evelyn Glennie and the winners of television's *Operatunity*, Denise Leigh and Jane Gilchrist, join the BBC Concert Orchestra under Carl Davis for the main part of the evening's entertainment in Hyde Park, and the Royal Choral Society leads the singing for the grand finale. The event is hosted once again by the inimitable Terry Wogan.

THE ROYAL PARKS

Saturday 11 September
Hyde Park. Gates open 4.00pm; entertainment on stage from 5.30pm

Tickets: £19.00 (under-3s free), available now by post/fax using the Booking Form facing page 130, by phone on 0870 899 8100 (24 hours, national rate) or online via www.bbc.co.uk/proms, and also (after 14 June) from the Royal Albert Hall on 020 7589 8212 (9.00am–9.00pm). A £2.25 transaction fee applies.

Corporate hospitality facilities are available. Call Charles Webb on 0870 720 3010.

BBC Proms in the Park, Manchester

Manchester joins the Last Night festivities for the first time with an event at URBIS in Cathedral Gardens, with music from the Hallé under John Wilson.

Saturday 11 September
URBIS, Cathedral Gardens, Manchester.
For free tickets, call 08700 100 300 (from 12 June).

BBC Proms in the Park, Belfast

Flautist James Galway, baritone Bruno Caproni and the Ulster Youth Choir are the guests of the Ulster Orchestra and Thierry Fischer for a concert in the grounds of City Hall in Donegall Square.

Saturday 11 September
Donegall Square, Belfast.
For free tickets, call 0870 333 1918; visit www.bbc.co.uk/ni/tickets; or write to: BBC NI Ticket Unit (Proms), Broadcasting House, Ormeau Avenue, Belfast BT2 8HQ.

BBC Proms in the Park, Glasgow

The BBC Scottish Symphony Orchestra returns to Glasgow's Pacific Quay for Scotland's second Prom in the Park.

Saturday 11 September
Pacific Quay, Glasgow.
For free tickets (max. six per request), call 08700 100 300 (from 1 July).

BBC Proms in the Park, Swansea

Proms in the Park returns to Swansea's Singleton Park for a concert presented by Aled Jones, featuring Welsh tenor Dennis O'Neill, Broadway star Kim Criswell, and the all-girl string quartet Celticana, accompanied by the BBC National Orchestra of Wales conducted by Grant Llewellyn.

Saturday 11 September
Singleton Park, Swansea.
Tickets: £6.50 in advance or £8.00 on the day (under-12s free), from the BBC Call NOW Line on 08700 13 1812 or the Grand Theatre Box Office on 01792 475715, or in person from the Grand Theatre Box Office, Singleton Street, Swansea.

Note that all BBC Proms in the Park events are outdoors and tickets are unreserved. The use of chairs is discouraged since it obstructs the view of others, but if you find it necessary because of limited mobility, please be considerate to your neighbours. In the interest of safety, please do not bring glass items, barbecues or flaming torches.

Tickets for BBC Proms in the Park, London, and the BBC Children's Prom in the Park can also be bought in person (no transaction fee) at the BBC Shops at 50 Margaret Street, London W1, and Bush House, Strand, London WC2

BBC Children's Prom in the Park celebrates Disney's Enchanted Evening
The fifth BBC Children's Prom in the Park promises to be a fantastic night as it takes you on a grand journey through some of Disney's greatest stories in an enchanted evening of animation and your favourite Disney songs. Pack up a picnic and join the BBC Concert Orchestra and all your Disney friends for a magical and memorable evening.

Sunday 12 September
Hyde Park. Gates open 5.00pm; entertainment on stage from 6.30pm; main concert 7.00pm–c8.30pm

Tickets: £12.00 (adults), £7.50 (children 3–16, under-3s free), available now by post/fax using the Booking Form facing page 130, by phone on 0870 899 8001 (24 hours, national rate) or online via www.bbc.co.uk/proms, and also (after 14 June) from the Royal Albert Hall on 020 7589 8212 (9.00am–9.00pm). A £2.25 transaction fee applies.

Proms Chamber Music

Mondays at 1.00pm
Lecture Theatre, Victoria & Albert Museum

Broadcast live on BBC Radio 3 and repeated the following Saturday at 12 noon

PCM 1	Monday 19 July 1.00pm – c2.00pm	PCM 2	Monday 26 July 1.00pm – c2.00pm	PCM 3	Monday 2 August 1.00pm – c2.00pm

The BBC Proms and the Victoria & Albert Museum continue their popular collaboration, presenting eight Monday-lunchtime concerts highlighting Proms artists, themes and anniversaries in the intimate setting of the Lecture Theatre at the V&A, a short walk from the Royal Albert Hall.
Hosted by Stephanie Hughes

How to Book
All tickets £8.00.
Advance booking is advised.

Before the day of the **concert** all bookings should be made with the Royal Albert Hall Box Office, *either* using the priority Booking Form *(facing page 130)*, the Online Ticket Request system (at www.bbc.co.uk/proms) or by telephone or in person (from Monday 14 June).

On the day of the concert tickets can only be bought *(subject to availability)* at the V&A, Exhibition Road entrance *(see map, page 122).*

Performing Art
Mondays, 12.15pm–c12.35pm (before Proms Chamber Music concerts)

Admission free to Proms Chamber Music ticket-holders

Available to listen to online from the morning after at www.bbc.co.uk/proms

Performing Art is back! In partnership with the V&A, the popular pre-concert talks return to shed new light on the shared world of art and music and to celebrate the V&A's unparalleled collection of decorative art and sculpture. Hosted by Christopher Cook in conversation with curators from the V&A, each talk will focus on a particular object that relates to the major themes of the season. And this year, for the first time, you can also listen to *Performing Art* talks, exclusively online, from the morning after.

Admission to the V&A is free. The museum and its restaurant are open from 10.00am.

Also at the V&A: Proms Composer Portraits. For details, see page 144.

PCM 1 — Monday 19 July

Janáček
String Quartet No. 1, 'The Kreutzer Sonata' *18'*

Dvořák
Piano Quintet in A major, Op. 81 *38'*

Škampa Quartet
Itamar Golan *piano*

Two composer anniversaries are celebrated with two chamber music masterpieces in the opening of this season's lunchtime series. The distinctive musical voice of Janáček is in powerful and mercurial mood for a quartet based on Tolstoy's tragic novella, *The Kreutzer Sonata*, while the abundant lyricism of Dvořák's maturity shines through his glorious quintet which mines the rich vein of Czech folk music.

📖 *Back to Bohemia, pages 18–23*

PCM 2 — Monday 26 July

Schubert
String Trio in B flat major, D471 *11'*

Mozart
String Quintet in C major, K515 *40'*

Pinchas Zukerman *violin*
Jessica Linnebach *violin*
Donnie Deacon *violin/viola*
Jethro Marks *viola*
Amanda Forsyth *cello*

Following his Proms appearance as soloist in Elgar's Violin Concerto (Prom 13), Pinchas Zukerman joins colleagues from the National Arts Centre Orchestra in Toronto, where he is Music Director, for two chamber music classics: a perfect miniature by Schubert, the product of his new-found freedom at the age of 19, and Mozart's most extended, superbly eloquent quintet, composed just before his final three symphonies.

PCM 3 — Monday 2 August

Dvořák
Moravian Duets – selection *10'*

Britten
On This Island *13'*

R. Strauss
Ständchen; Morgen; Hat gesagt; Mit deinen blauen Augen; Ich trage meine Minne; Wie sollten wir geheim sie halten *14'*

Dvořák
Moravian Duets – selection *10'*

Sally Matthews *soprano*
Ailish Tynan *soprano*
Iain Burnside *piano*

Two leading young members of Radio 3's New Generation Artists team up for Dvořák's piquant duets exploring the everyday lives and loves of a people rooted in the natural world. Solo contributions come from the young Britten in the 1930s, revelling in setting poems by his friend W. H. Auden, and that supreme lover of the soprano voice, Strauss, with a selection of favourite songs.

📖 *Back to Bohemia, pages 18–23; Proms Artists, pages 80–85*

PCM 4 — Monday 9 August 1.00pm – c2.00pm

PCM 5 — Monday 16 August 1.00pm – c2.00pm

PCM 6 — Monday 23 August 1.00pm – c2.00pm

PCM 7 — Monday 30 August 1.00pm – c2.00pm

PCM 8 — Monday 6 September 1.00pm – c2.00pm

PCM 4

Chopin
Scherzo in C sharp minor, Op. 39   8'

Debussy
Estampes   14'

Janáček
In the Mists   17'

Skryabin
Piano Sonata No. 5   8'

Llŷr Williams piano

An acclaimed Radio 3 New Generation Artist presents a programme centring on two Proms themes. East meets West for Debussy with the sounds of the gamelan and the lure of Moorish romance, while Janáček's world has a Czech introspection and wistfulness laced with pent-up energy. Chopin's impetuous narrative and Skryabin's extraordinary sonorities – 'I bring audacity' – complete a kaleidoscopic mix.

📖 EAST/WEST, pages 4–12; Back to Bohemia, pages 18–23; Proms Artists, pages 80–85

PCM 5

Programme to include:

Debussy
Cello Sonata

Jia Da Qun
The Prospect of Colored Desert

Kayhan Kalhor
Gallop of a Thousand Horses

Yo-Yo Ma cello
Silk Road Ensemble

Rounding off a weekend of Proms events (Proms 38 and 40), this ground-breaking ensemble, which takes its cue from the ancient and exotic trading route through China and Central Asia, turns to the more intimate side of its repertoire including pieces for solo pipa, sheng, kemanche and string quartet, and musicians from China and Kyrgyzstan. Yo-Yo Ma's starting-point for his collective musical adventure was the question: 'What happens when strangers meet?' The answer: a rich global circulation of musical ideas.

📖 EAST/WEST, pages 4–12

PCM 6

Schmelzer
Sonatae unarum fidium – Sonata No. 4   10'

Biber
Mystery (Rosary) Sonatas: No. 1, 'The Annunciation'; No. 6, 'The Agony in the Garden'; No. 10, 'The Crucifixion'   27'

interspersed with:

Froberger
Suite in C   6'

Lamentation 'Ferdinand le troisième'   6'

Andrew Manze violin
Richard Egarr harpsichord/ chamber organ

After directing the English Concert (Prom 47), Andrew Manze performs a set of extraordinary, innovative sonatas with his regular duo partner. Anniversary composer Biber explores the joyful and sorrowful mysteries of the rosary with unique intensity, aided by audacious re-tunings of the violin, while Froberger, his contemporary, brings a new confidence and range of expression to keyboard writing.

📖 Back to Bohemia, pages 18–23

PCM 7

Messiaen
Le merle noir   6'

Ives
'Concord' Sonata   48'

Pierre-Laurent Aimard piano
Emily Beynon flute

Fifty years after his death, Ives still sounds like the most thrillingly contemporary composer, his music new-minted and visionary. For him it was part of the spiritual language of nature, and in a work which he endlessly revised he pays tribute to a group of transcendental American philosophers in a small town in New England in the mid-19th century. Thoreau's simple, pastoral flute, heard briefly at the end of 'Concord', takes flight in Messiaen's joyous birdsong.

📖 Season Highlights, pages 62–3

PCM 8

Janáček
Concertino   16'

Dallapiccola
Piccola musica notturna   7'

Simon Holt
The Coroner's Report   c10'
BBC commission: world premiere

Martinů
La revue de cuisine   15'

Rolf Hind piano
Britten Sinfonia
Nicholas Daniel oboe/conductor

A buoyant end to the series with the energy of Janáček's adventurous piece for solo piano and ensemble – a work he originally planned to call 'Springtime' – and Martinů's witty ballet score peopled with kitchen utensils! Anniversary composer Dallapiccola adds a little magical stillness and solitude, while Simon Holt's new work is plain mystery: its different sections are labelled 'Exhibits A to H'. Evidence … but of what?

📖 Back to Bohemia, pages 18–23; New Music, pages 46–52

Getting to the Royal Albert Hall

The following buses stop where indicated:

No. 9 to Charing Cross and Aldwych
No. 10 to Euston and King's Cross
No. 52 to Victoria

No. 9 to Hammersmith
No. 10 to Hammersmith
No. 52 to Notting Hill and Willesden

(all these buses operate as Night Buses after midnight)

No. 360 to/from South Kensington, Pimlico, Vauxhall and Elephant & Castle

Please note that the Royal Albert Hall lies outside the Congestion Charging Zone

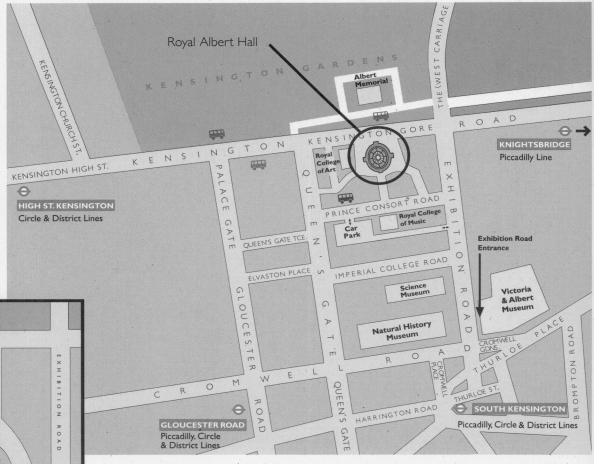

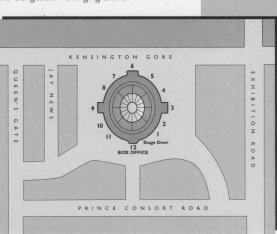

Every Prom live on BBC Radio 3 and www.bbc.co.uk/proms

How to Prom

What is Promming?

The popular tradition of Promming is central to the unique and informal atmosphere of the BBC Proms.

Up to 1,400 standing places are available at each Proms concert. The traditionally low prices allow you to enjoy world-class concerts for just £4.00 each (or even less with a Season Ticket or Weekend Promming Pass).

There are two standing areas: the Arena, which is located directly in front of the stage, and the Gallery, running round the top of the Hall. All spaces are unreserved.

Day Prommers

Over 500 Arena and Gallery tickets (priced £4.00) go on sale on the day 30 minutes before doors open (one hour before on days when there are Pre-Prom talks). These tickets cannot be booked in advance, so even if all seats have been sold, you always have a good chance of getting in (though early queuing is obviously advisable for the more popular concerts). You must buy your ticket in person.

Wheelchair-users who wish to Prom in the Gallery should queue in the same way but will be redirected to Door 8 once their ticket is purchased. (For further information for disabled concert-goers see page 126)

Day tickets are available (for cash only) at Door 11 (Arena) and Door 10 (Gallery), not at the Box Office. If in doubt about where to go, Royal Albert Hall stewards will point you in the right direction.

Season Tickets

Frequent Prommers can save money by purchasing Arena or Gallery Season Tickets covering either the whole Proms season or only the first or second half (ie Proms 1–37 or Proms 38–73).

Season Ticket-holders benefit from:
- guaranteed entrance (until 10 minutes before each concert)
- great savings – prices can work out at less than £2.00 per concert
- guaranteed entrance to the Last Night for Whole Season Ticket-holders and special access to a reserved allocation of Last Night tickets for Half Season Ticket-holders. *See page 127.*

Please note that Season Ticket-holders arriving at the Royal Albert Hall later than 10 minutes before a concert are not guaranteed entry and may be asked, in certain circumstances, to join the day queue.

For further details and prices of Season Tickets, see page 129.

For further details and prices of Weekend Promming Passes, see page 98.

Where to Queue

- Arena Day Queue
  Enter by Door 11

- Gallery Day Queue
  Enter by Door 10

- Arena Season Queue
  Enter by Door 1

- Gallery Season Queue
  Enter by Door 2

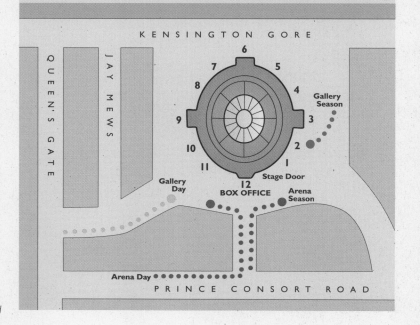

At the Royal Albert Hall: new for 2004

Royal Albert Hall Tours
Following its £70m, eight-year redevelopment programme, the Royal Albert Hall now offers tours through the iconic building, revealing its hidden history. Highlights include the auditorium, exclusive access to the Royal Retiring Room, a look inside the Queen's Box and a presentation showing the huge range of events that take place at the Hall. As the Hall is a working venue, each tour is unique and may include opportunities to see rehearsals or the technical preparations for a show. *Please note that the tours do not include a visit to the backstage area.*

Tours run from 10.00am, with the last tour at 3.30pm, from Friday to Tuesday inclusive. Tours depart from inside the South Porch at Door 12 and last around 45 minutes. Telephone the Hall to check times and for further information.

Tour tickets can be purchased from the Royal Albert Hall Box Office by telephoning 020 7838 3105, online at www.royalalberthall.com or in person from the Box Office at Door 12.
Adult: £6.00; Child (under 16): £3.50; Under-5s: free; Senior Citizen/Student: £5.00; Disabled people: £3.00; Family (up to 2 adults and 3 children): £16.00
Please note: 25p per ticket is charged for all purchases made by phone or online.

Groups of 10 or more can claim a 15% discount. Advance booking is recommended for large parties. There is a maximum of 15 people per tour.

Access The Royal Albert Hall is a large building with five floors. The tour covers moderate distances, including several staircases. Lifts are available and the tour is fully accessible to wheelchair-users. If you will require use of the lifts or have additional access requirements, please notify the Box Office when booking your tour ticket.

Tour terms and conditions The Royal Albert Hall is a working performing arts venue. As such, tours are subject to availability and may be cancelled or curtailed at short notice.

Royal Albert Hall Shop
The new Royal Albert Hall Shop, offering a selection of Royal Albert Hall gifts and souvenirs, is located in the South Porch at Door 12.
The Shop is open daily from 10.00am to 5.00pm.
Tour visitors can claim a 10% discount on selected merchandise on presentation of their tour ticket.

Note that Proms Merchandise can also be purchased at Door 6 foyer, once the audience is admitted to the Hall.

Entrance for Box Office and Tours: Door 12

Eating & drinking

Restaurants

The Royal Albert Hall has three restaurants catering for all tastes, from light meals to three-course dinners.

Pre-concert refreshments

All restaurants open two hours before the start of the performance.

The Elgar Restaurant offers a two or three-course menu with full table service. Tables in the Elgar Restaurant are bookable in advance on 020 7838 3101. Enter via Door 8 to the Circle level.

The Café Consort offers a full menu including salads, sandwiches and light meals and is now also open during the daytime offering coffee and a selection of light meals. Enter via Door 12 to the Grand Tier level.

The Victoria Brasserie has a menu including light starters, pizza and pasta dishes, and a range of desserts. Enter via Door 1 to the Circle level.

Catering in your box

From sandwiches to a two-course supper including a full range of beverages, box hospitality can be pre-ordered by telephoning 020 7589 5666. Please allow two working days' notice.

Please note that you are not permitted to consume your own food and drink in the Hall. In the interests of Health & Safety, glasses and bottles are not allowed in the auditorium except as part of box hospitality ordered through the Hall's caterers.

Bars

Bars are located on every floor and all offer a full range of alcoholic and soft drinks, hot beverages, ice cream, confectionery and sandwiches.

The Champagne and North Circle Bars open two hours before the start of the performance, offering a range of sandwiches. A small amount of seating is available. Enter via Door 1 to the Grand Tier and Circle levels respectively.

The following bars open 45 minutes before the start of the performance:

The Lanson Arena Bar is located in the Arena Foyers, sub-basement level. Enter via Door 1.

The Door 6 and 7 Bars are located at ground level. Enter via Door 6.

The Porch Bars are located at ground level. Enter via Door 3 or 9.

The Grand Tier Bars are located at Grand Tier level. Enter via Door 3 or 9.

The Second Tier Bar is located at Second Tier level. Enter via Door 3.

Dos and don'ts at the Hall

Doors open 45 minutes before each concert (earlier for restaurant access).

Latecomers will not be admitted into the auditorium unless or until there is a suitable break in the music. There is a video monitor with digital audio relay in the foyer at Door 6.

Bags and coats may be left in the cloakrooms at Door 9 (ground level), Door 8 (Circle level) and at basement level. Folding chairs and hand-luggage larger than a briefcase are not allowed in the auditorium.

Children under 5 In consideration of our audience and artists, children under the age of 5 are not allowed in the auditorium. Children between the ages of 5 and 16 are positively encouraged (see *Special Offers, page 98*).

Car Parking A limited number of parking spaces are available from 6.00pm in the Imperial College Car Park (Prince Consort or Exhibition Road entrances). These can be booked in advance (priced £7.50) by ticking the appropriate column on the Priority Booking Form (facing page 130) or by telephoning the Box Office (open 9.00am–9.00pm daily, from 14 June) on 020 7589 8212. Please note that, if attending both early-evening and late-night concerts, only one parking fee is payable.

Dress Code There is no dress code at the Proms.

Mobile phones and watch alarms must be turned off.

The use of cameras, video cameras and recording equipment is strictly forbidden.

Eating and drinking are not permitted inside the auditorium.

Smoking The Royal Albert Hall has a new policy with regard to smoking and from July 2004 will restrict smoking within the building to the following areas only: North Circle Bar; Bars and Foyers at Door 3 (including the ground-floor foyer but not the East Porch bar); Lanson Arena Bar.

Notice Boards Notice boards with Proms news and programme and artist updates are located around the Hall.

Information for disabled concert-goers

Access at the Proms

Call the **Access Information Line** on **020 7838 3110** for advice on facilities for disabled concert-goers (including car parking) at all Proms venues; if you have any special requirements; or to request a Royal Albert Hall Access leaflet. Dedicated staff will be available daily from 9.00am to 9.00pm. The Access leaflet is also available from the RAH website – www.royalalberthall.com.

 Wheelchair access is available at all Proms venues, but advance booking is advised.

The Royal Albert Hall has up to 14 spaces bookable in the Stalls for wheelchair-users and their companions (entrance via Door 8). End-of-aisle places are priced as Centre Stalls seats; front-row platform spaces either side of the stage are priced as Side Stalls seats; rear platform places are priced as Front Circle seats. There are up to six spaces in the Front Circle, priced as such. When filling in the Booking Form, tick your preferred price range (ie Centre Stalls, Side Stalls or Front Circle) and enter the number of places required under the 'Wheelchair space' column.

Four wheelchair spaces are now available in the Gallery for Promming. These cannot be pre-booked. (See page 123 for 'How to Prom'.)

For other Proms venues, spaces can be reserved by calling **020 7838 3110**.

Passenger lifts at the Royal Albert Hall are located off the ground-floor corridor at Doors 1 and 8. Use of lifts is discouraged during performances.

Booking

Disabled concert-goers (and a companion) receive a 50% discount on all ticket prices (except Arena and Gallery areas) for concerts at the Royal Albert Hall and for Proms Chamber Music concerts at the V&A. To claim this discount, tick the 'Disabled' box at the end of the Booking Form, or call the Access Information Line on **020 7838 3110** if booking by phone (from Monday 14 June).

Tickets can also be purchased in person from Monday 14 June at the Royal Albert Hall. The Box Office is situated at Door 12 and has ramped access, and induction loop and drop down counters.

 The Royal Albert Hall has an infra-red system with a number of personal receivers for use with and without hearing aids. To make use of the service, collect a free receiver from the Door 6 Information Desk.

 If you have a guide dog, the best place to sit in the Royal Albert Hall is in a Loggia or Second Tier Box, where your dog may stay with you. If you are sitting elsewhere, stewards will be happy to look after your dog while you enjoy

the concert. Please call the Access Information Line on **020 7838 3110** to organise in advance of your visit.

Proms Guide: non-print versions

Audio cassette, CD, braille and computer disk versions of this Guide are available in two parts, 'Concerts Listings' and 'Articles', priced £2.50 each or £5 for both.

For more information and to order, contact RNIB Customer Services: 0845 7023 153.

Radio 3 commentary

Visually-impaired patrons are welcome to use the free infra-red hearing facility (see above) to listen in to the broadcast commentary on Radio 3.

Programme-reading service

Ask at the Door 6 Information Desk if you would like a steward to read your programme out to you.

Large-print programmes & texts

Large-print concert programmes can be made available on the night (at the same price as the standard programme) if ordered not less than five working days in advance. Complimentary large-print texts and opera librettos can also be made available on the night (where applicable) if ordered in advance. To order any large-print programmes or texts, please telephone 020 7765 3260. They will be left for collection at the Door 6 Information Desk 45 minutes before the start of the concert.

The Last Night

Owing to the huge demand for Last Night tickets, special booking arrangements apply. Your best chance of purchasing tickets for the Last Night of the Proms is through the Priority Booking system

Priority Booking for the Last Night

The Six Concert Rule
In order to apply for any tickets for the Last Night during the Priority Booking period (ie before General Booking opens on Monday 14 June), you must book for at least six other concerts in the 2004 season.

Book one ticket in the same seating area for at least six other concerts in the 2004 season and you can apply at the same time for a single ticket in the same seating area for the Last Night. For example, book a ticket in the Choir for six concerts, and you can apply for one ticket in the Choir for the Last Night.

Book two or more tickets in the same seating area for at least six other concerts in the 2004 season and you can apply at the same time for a maximum of two tickets in the same seating area for the Last Night (ie whether you book two or 22 Stalls tickets for six concerts, you can still apply for only two Stalls tickets for the Last Night).

Note that, if you book tickets for at least six other concerts but in different seating areas, you will be allocated Last Night seats in the area of the majority of your bookings (unless you specify that lower-priced tickets are desired).

We regret that, if the Last Night is sold out by the time your application is processed, no refunds for other tickets purchased will be payable.

General Booking for the Last Night

Once General Booking opens (on Monday 14 June), the 'Six Concert Rule' no longer applies. Note, however, that Last Night tickets have usually sold out by this stage.

Please note that, for all Last Night bookings, only one application (for a maximum of two tickets) can be made per household.

Promming at the Last Night

Day Prommers and Weekend Promming Pass holders who have attended six or more other concerts (in either the Arena or the Gallery) can buy one ticket each for the Last Night (priced £4.00) on presentation of their used tickets at the Box Office on or after Wednesday 21 July (subject to availability).

Season Ticket-holders Whole Season Tickets include admission to the Last Night. A limited allocation of Last Night places is also reserved for Half Season Ticket-holders. Holders of First Half Season Tickets can buy one ticket each (priced £4.00) at the Box Office from Wednesday 21 July (subject to availability). Holders of Second Half

Season Tickets can buy tickets in the same way from Wednesday 18 August (subject to availability).

Queuing Whole Season Ticket-holders and other Prommers with Last Night tickets are guaranteed entrance until 10 minutes before the concert. All Prommers (Day or Season) with Last Night tickets should queue at Door 1 (Arena) or Door 2 (Gallery).

Sleeping Out There has long been a tradition of Prommers with Last Night tickets sleeping out overnight to secure their preferred standing place in the Arena. The official queues will form at 4.00pm on the last Friday of the season at Door 1 (Arena) and Door 2 (Gallery). Those also wishing to attend Prom 73 will be given numbered slips to reserve their places in the queue but must return in person immediately after the end of the concert.

On the Night A number of standing tickets are available on the Last Night itself (priced £4.00), one per person, just before the start of the concert. No previous ticket purchases are necessary. Just join the queue at Door 11 (Arena) or Door 10 (Gallery) and you may well be lucky.

Choose your seating area

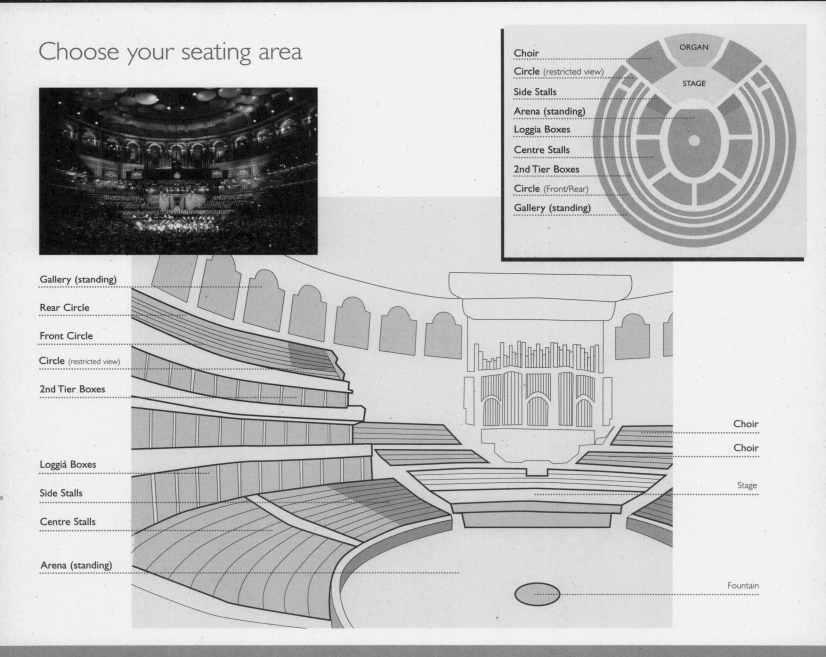

Choir
Circle (restricted view)
Side Stalls
Arena (standing)
Loggia Boxes
Centre Stalls
2nd Tier Boxes
Circle (Front/Rear)
Gallery (standing)

ORGAN

STAGE

Gallery (standing)

Rear Circle

Front Circle

Circle (restricted view)

2nd Tier Boxes

Loggià Boxes

Side Stalls

Centre Stalls

Arena (standing)

Choir

Choir

Stage

Fountain

Price Bands for Proms in the Royal Albert Hall

Seats

Each concert falls into one of seven different price bands, colour coded for easy reference

	A	B	C	D	E	F	G
Centre Stalls	£23.00	£30.00	£38.00	£12.50	£15.00	£73.00	
Side Stalls	£21.50	£27.00	£35.00	£12.50	£15.00	£70.00	
Loggia Boxes (8 seats)	£25.00	£32.50	£40.00	£12.50	£15.00	£75.00	
2nd Tier Boxes (5 seats)	£17.50	£22.50	£32.00	£12.50	£15.00	£70.00	ALL SEATS £10.00 (UNDER-16s £5.00)
Choir	£15.00	£18.00	£24.00	£9.00	£12.50	£52.50	
Front Circle	£13.00	£16.00	£20.00	£9.00	£12.50	£52.50	
Rear Circle	£10.00	£11.00	£14.50	£9.00	£12.50	£40.00	
Circle (restricted view)	£6.00	£7.00	£10.00			£20.00	

Promming

Standing places are available in the Arena and Gallery on the day for £4.00 (see page 123)

	Dates	Arena	Gallery
Season Tickets			
Whole Season (Proms 1–74)	16 July – 11 September	**£160.00**	**£135.00**
Half Season tickets			
First Half (Proms 1–37)	16 July – 12 August	**£90.00**	**£75.00**
Second Half (Proms 38–73)	13 August – 10 September	**£90.00**	**£75.00**

BBC Proms in the Park, London, Saturday 11 September

All tickets £19.00   (for further details of this and other Proms in the Park venues, see page 119)

BBC Children's Prom in the Park Celebrates Disney's Enchanted Evening, London, Sunday 12 September

Adults £12.00   **Children (3–16 yrs) £7.50**   **Under-3s free**

Please note that booking fees apply to all postal, fax, telephone and online bookings (for details, see Booking Form)

Tickets cannot be exchanged for other performances nor refunded except in the event of a cancelled performance.

Express booking

All booking forms that include a request for an A band concert qualify for express booking. To increase your chances of getting the tickets you want for popular concerts in price bands B and C, you should book for an A band concert too. If you are booking for the *Blue Peter Prom* (price band G), your booking will also qualify for express booking. Tick the box at the end of the Booking Form if your application qualifies.

Disabled concert-goers

See page 126 for details of special discounts, access and facilities.

Privately owned seats

A high proportion of boxes, as well as 650 Stalls seats, are privately owned. Unless returned by owners, these seats are not available for sale.

Season tickets

Season tickets can be booked by post, fax or online from 17 May and by phone or in person at the Box Office from 14 June. For postal and fax bookings, complete the special section of the Booking Form (*facing page 130*). Two passport-sized photographs must be provided before tickets can be issued.

Proms Chamber Music

All seats £8.00, bookable in advance using the Booking Form (*facing page 130*) or via the Proms website.

Free events

Tickets for Proms Composer Portraits are free and can be collected at the Proms Information Desk at the V&A (Exhibition Road entrance) from an hour beforehand.
Pre-Prom Talks are free to ticket-holders for that evening's concert.

How to fill in the Priority Booking Form

- **Choose the concerts** you want to go to and where you want to sit.

- **Enter the number of tickets** you require for each concert under your chosen seating area.

- **Add up the value of tickets** requested and enter the amount in the 'Sub-total' column.

- **For Special Offers** (see *page 98*) tick the 'discount claimed' column and enter the value of the discount in the 'Discount' column. Subtract the value of the discount from the sub-total and enter the 'Total' at the end of the row.

- **For Under-16 discounts** (see *page 98*) enter the number of adults within the white area, the number of under-16s within the blue area.

- **If the tickets you want are not available**, lower-priced tickets for the same concert will be sent. Please tick the box at the end of the Booking Form if this is not acceptable.

Booking Queries
If you have any queries about how to fill in the Booking Form, call the Box Office on 020 7589 8212 (open 9.00am–9.00pm daily).

Fax Booking
If booking by fax, clearly state your name on all three pages. Please note that fax booking lines are open 24 hours a day. Please do not duplicate your booking by post or online.

Online Booking
For details of how to book online, visit the BBC Proms website at www.bbc.co.uk/proms

PRIORITY BOOKING FORM PART 1

Full name of sender (fax bookings only)   Surname **HALL**   First Name **ALBERT**

Seating Area: please indicate number of tickets required

Prom	Date	Time	Price Code	Special Offers	Centre Stalls	Side Stalls	Loggia Boxes	2nd Tier Boxes	Front Circle	Rear Circle	Circle	Wheelchair space	Sub-total (£)	Please tick if discount claimed	Discount (£)	Car Parking	Total (£)	Office Use
1	Friday 16 July	7.30	B															
2	Saturday 17 July	7.00	A															
3	Sunday 18 July	6.30	A															
4	Monday 19 July	7.00	A															
5	Monday 19 July	10.00	D															
6	Tuesday 20 July	7.30	A															
7	Wednesday 21 July	7.30	A		2													
8	Thursday 22 July	7.30	A										46:00				46:00	
9	Friday 23 July	7.30	A															
10	Saturday 24 July	11.00	G															
11	Saturday 24 July	7.30	A															
12	Sunday 25 July	3.30	G															
13	Sunday 25 July	7.30	A															
14	Monday 26 July	7.30	A															
15	Tuesday 27 July	7.30	A		10													
16	Wednesday 28 July	7.00	A										216:00	✓	21:50		193:50	
17	Wednesday 28 July	10.00	D															
18	Thursday 29 July	7.30	A															
19	Friday 30 July	7.30	C															
20	Saturday 31 July	7.30	C															
21	Saturday 31 July	7.00	C				2 2						40:00	✓	20:00		60:00	
22	Sunday 1 August	10.00	E															
23	Sunday 1 August	6.30	D	2														
24	Monday 2 August	9.00	D	2									46:00				46:00	
		7.30	A										25:00	✓	8:00		17:00	

49	Sunday 22 August	10.00	D															
50	Monday 23 August	6.30	A															
51	Monday 23 August	7.00	B															
52	Tuesday 24 August	10.00	E															
53	Wednesday 25 August	7.30	B															
		7.00	A															
54	Wednesday 25 August	10.00	D															

Total to carry over **362:50**

PRIORITY BOOKING FORM PART 3

Full name of sender (fax bookings only)   Surname **HALL**   First Name **ALBERT**

BBC Proms in the Park, London, Saturday 11 September
For details of this and other Proms in the Park venues, see page 119

	Number of tickets	Total (£)
All tickets £19.00 (under-3s free)		Sub-total

BBC Children's Prom in the Park Celebrates Disney's Enchanted Evening
London, Sunday 12 September
For details, see page 119

	Number of tickets	Total (£)
Adult tickets £12.00		
Child tickets (3–16 yrs): £7.50 (under-3s free)		Sub-total

Part 3 Total £

Parts 1&2 Total	Part 3 Total	Booking fee	
Sum of totals £ 362:50	+ £	+ £2.25 = Grand Total £ 364:75

BBC Proms in the Park

For the second year running, audiences in all four nations of the UK get to share in the unique festive atmosphere of the Last Night of the Proms, as the ninth season of BBC Proms in the Park reaches out beyond London to Belfast, Glasgow, Swansea and, for the first time, Manchester too

RIGHT
Last Night line-up: James Galway and his golden flute, with the Ulster Orchestra's Principal Conductor, Thierry Fischer, in Belfast; and Kim Criswell, Aled Jones and Dennis O'Neill in Swansea …

BELOW
… and headlining in Hyde Park are: Evelyn Glennie, Carl Davis, and Denise Leigh and Jane Gilchrist, the joint winners of TV's *Operatunity*

Once again BBC Proms in the Park will be bursting out all over on the Last Night of the 2004 season. The electric atmosphere of this unique event returns to London, Glasgow, Swansea and Belfast – and this year, for the first time, spreads its embrace to encompass Manchester as well. All five BBC Proms in the Park events culminate in live big-screen link-ups with the Royal Albert Hall, giving the whole country the chance to bob up and down and unite in song.

Every year, audiences have flocked to BBC Proms in the Park in some of the country's most enticing outdoor venues, relishing the chance to picnic, participate and enjoy some sumptuous music-making as summer draws to its end. This year will be no exception, as the star performers around the country will include dynamic percussionist Evelyn Glennie and the joint winners of television's *Operatunity* contest (in London), heroic tenor Dennis O'Neill and Broadway diva Kim Criswell (in Swansea), and legendary flautist James Galway (in Belfast). Celebrity hosts such as the irrepressible Terry Wogan (in London) and Aled Jones (in Wales) are also on hand to guide you through a magical night of sheer enjoyment and full-throated song, culminating in the traditional singalong sequence of national songs. There's no better night out, and no better way to enjoy the Last Night of the Proms.

Events sponsored by
RENAULT

BBC Proms in the Park
Saturday 11 September
in London, Manchester, Belfast, Glasgow and Swansea
For further details and booking information,
see page 119

BBC Children's Prom in the Park celebrates Disney's Enchanted Evening

Once again, the musical magic continues even after the Proms are over, with a special children's concert of animated classics

The fifth BBC Children's Prom in the Park promises a magical evening's entertainment as the BBC Concert Orchestra and a host of up-and-coming guest artists take you on a whimsical tour through some of Disney's greatest stories.

Disney films have always been able to transport audiences to magical places. Now, for one night only, London's Hyde Park will be transformed into a world of make-believe that will capture the hearts of both young and old, as stunning soundtrack arrangements and big-screen animation combine in a 90-minute concert to bring your favourite Disney characters to life.

So come along to Hyde Park, on the night after the Last Night of the Proms, and you too can fly through the streets of Agraba with Aladdin and Jasmine, waltz in a beautiful French castle with Belle and the Beast, and discover an underwater paradise with Ariel and Sebastian.

It's a night out under the stars, so pack up your family, friends and a picnic – let Disney provide the pixie dust – and be our guest for a once-in-a-lifetime experience.

**BBC Children's Prom in the Park celebrates Disney's Enchanted Evening
Sunday 12 September**
in Hyde Park, London
*For further details and
booking information, see page 119*

THE ROYAL PARKS

B&W Bowers & Wilkins

> *ABSORBED*

With every beautiful note
I'm where I want to be

Listen and you'll see

THE NEW B&W
700

Wider still and wider...

Peter Kingston, Further Education Editor of *The Guardian*, reveals how the BBC Proms are going out of their way to bring new audiences in

Whatever else the world's most celebrated music festival means to the millions who have enjoyed it, the BBC Proms are – and always have been – about accessibility.

These high summer concerts, night after night in the Royal Albert Hall, blew away long ago the aura of stiffness and stuffiness that other promoters of classical music have lately been trying to dispel.

For a start, they are reasonably priced and there's no dress code. Provided you are prepared to stand, you can just walk in and hear some of the finest musicians on the planet.

But there's a new generation now who may wish to be led towards these riches. And so the folk at the BBC Proms have been trying to nurture their audience. Very wisely, they aim much of this effort at the young and families.

This year there are four schemes: Proms Out and About, Silk Road Tales, two Blue Peter Proms, and the annual BBC Proms/Guardian Young Composers Competition. 'They're a mixture of bringing people into the Hall and also going out of the Hall to take the Proms to people and to interest them in wanting to come in and see what the Proms are all about,' explains Kate Finch, Marketing Manager at the BBC Proms.

Proms Out and About

Proms Out and About will build on an inspiring idea tried for the first time last year. The idea is simple: take the BBC Symphony Orchestra to a venue where such an orchestra would not normally perform – last year it was the Brixton Academy in south London – and have it do its stuff in front of an invited audience from the local area, made up of people who might not have been to a concert or ever heard an orchestra live before.

As Doug Buist, BBC Proms Marketing and Audience Development Officer, explains: 'It's to give children and their parents, who haven't had the chance to experience an orchestra live before, the opportunity to do so, presented in such a way that it breaks down some of the barriers to attending concerts.'

In Brixton last year, in the run-up to the event, Proms staff visited schools, youth clubs and housing estate community centres. They usually went accompanied by a musician or three.

About 1,200 people subsequently turned up at the Academy to hear top American composer John Adams – perhaps the most performed classical composer alive – explain the workings of an orchestra and conduct pieces by Bartók, Bernstein, Britten, Copland and Stravinsky, as well as his own runaway hit, *Short Ride in a Fast Machine*. All were offered a deal to attend a selected group of Proms: about 300 took up the offer.

This year the exercise is being repeated, not just once, but twice. On 6 May, the BBC Symphony Orchestra goes to Hammersmith Town Hall in west London, and on 23 June the BBC Concert Orchestra goes to the Hackney Empire in east London.

'This is a real innovation for the Proms,' says Director, Nicholas Kenyon. 'We want to meet the audience in new venues and interact with them. Now that all the BBC orchestras have appointed Learning Managers, there's no limit to what we can achieve over the next few years.'

Silk Road Tales

The Silk Road Tales project draws inspiration from the British Library's summer exhibition *The Silk Road: Trade, Travel, War and Faith (see pages 142–3)*, and from the work of the cellist Yo-Yo Ma's Silk Road Project, which he set up in 1998 to study the ebb and flow of different cultural ideas along the ancient network of trade routes that connected Europe to Asia *(see pages 11–12)*.

ABOVE
Top American composer/ conductor John Adams with the BBC SO at last year's 'Out and About' concert in Brixton Academy

BOTTOM RIGHT
A sea of happy faces: John Adams and a young audience at the Brixton Academy

The project, which is divided into four strands, involves approximately 120 youngsters aged 13–17 from Chinese, Asian, Turkish, white and other communities in London and elsewhere in the UK. They will be brought together for a special event at the Shaw Theatre, in central London, on Saturday 14 August. This will include a one-hour stage performance of the youngsters' work and a 45-minute interactive presentation by Yo-Yo Ma and the Silk Road Ensemble. The following day the participants and their families are invited to attend the afternoon Prom being given by Ma and the Ensemble (Prom 40). Again it is anticipated that many will be attending their first formal concert.

Blue Peter Prom

BELOW
The Kagemusha Taiko drummers, appearing at this year's two Blue Peter Proms

What has become a sure-fire staple, the Blue Peter Prom, will happen twice this year. On the morning of Saturday 24 July and the following afternoon (Proms 10 and 12), those acoustic Albert Hall mushrooms will shiver to the cheers of hordes of children. The BBC Philharmonic will present suitably zippy programmes, conducted by its Italian-born Principal Conductor, Gianandrea Noseda, and its new Anglo-Chinese Assistant Conductor, Jason Lai, with guest appearances by the exciting Kagemusha Taiko drummers.

BBC Proms/Guardian Young Composers Competition

This year sees the sixth BBC Proms/ Guardian Young Composers Competition. It has established itself as the unique national contest for young people aged 11–18 who write music. The rules are simple: compose a piece no longer than five minutes in any style – classical, rock, jazz, funk, garage, whatever – and for any combination of voice(s) and/or instrument(s).

All entrants – last year there were nearly 500 – are invited up for a special Young Composers Day at the Proms on Monday 2 August. The day includes live performances of the winning pieces, free entry to that night's concert (Prom 24) and, crucially, a chance for all the young people to meet others who share their interest. They also have the opportunity, which they usually grab with vim, to quiz a panel of composers from the worlds of classical music, film, television and pop.

Like all these vital initiatives, this competition is not only about audience-building, but about music-building, ensuring the survival of this wonderful art for the future.

BBC Proms Out and About

Thursday 6 May, 6.30pm
Hammersmith Town Hall, London W6

Wednesday 23 June, 6.00m
Hackney Empire, London E8
Call 08700 100 300 for ticketing information

BBC Proms/Guardian Young Composers Concert

Monday 2 August, 4.30pm
Lecture Theatre,
Victoria & Albert Museum

Admission by invitation only:
call 020 7765 5575
or e-mail proms@bbc.co.uk

The winning works will be broadcast by BBC Radio 3 on *In Tune* (weekdays 5.00–7.30pm) during the Proms season

For more information about all Proms educational activities, visit www.bbc.co.uk/proms

The golden road to Samarkand

Experience a Silk Road summer at the British Library's major exhibition

The Silk Road:
Trade, Travel, War and Faith
The British Library, in collaboration
with the British Museum
Sponsored by the Pidem Fund
Open daily, 7 May to 12 September
Admission free

The Silk Road was a complex network of trade routes extending for over 6,000km, from the shores of the Mediterranean through the fabled central Asian cities of Bukhara and Samarkand to the heartland of China. For over 2,000 years it has attracted people wishing to make money, converts, diplomatic deals, conquests – or simply to find a quiet place of retreat. Today the name continues to beguile. It conjures up images of exotic cities, gorgeous silks and other luxuries, and of people and lives far removed from us in time, space and experience. Yet, as this new exhibition shows, the residents of the oasis Silk Road kingdoms and the journeying monks, merchants, soldiers and other travellers shared concerns that are familiar to us all.
In the first millennium AD, Silk Road residents

were part of a global economy that brought them into contact with a vast array of material goods: silks, spices and perfumes, precious stones and all manner of commodities. But they were also influenced by new faiths, literature, myths, ideas, technologies, arts and sciences. The exhibition's 400 manuscripts, artefacts and sounds, assembled from collections worldwide, aim to highlight this extraordinary weaving of cultures that formed the backdrop to lives along the Silk Road.

Music was one of the great Silk Road travellers: drummers and horn players accompanied armies on the march; travelling bands on camels and carts offered entertainment at the many festivals; Silk Road restaurants employed dancing girls and singers; while music was an integral part of Buddhist and other religious services. The origins of the violin and the Chinese *pipa* (lute) can be traced back to the Central Asian steppes. Itinerant musicians brought knowledge of new instruments and unfamiliar musical forms, traditions, songs and dances. Musical exhibits include: 10th-century notation; paintings of orchestras; figurines of dancers and musicians; fragmentary remains of a third-century lute; over 20 recordings of music, some of which trace their ancestry back to the eighth-century Silk Road.

Other highlights of the exhibition include: the world's earliest dated printed book, a copy of the Buddhist *Diamond Sutra* from 868 AD; the world's earliest manuscript chart of the skies with over 1,500 recognisable stars; an exquisitely carved sixth-century funerary couch; a Chinese almanac from 59 BC; vividly coloured 1,000-year-old silk textiles and woollen rugs.

For more information on the exhibition and the BL/Proms Silk Road Tales project, plus a chance to win a holiday to the Silk Road (courtesy of the China Travel Service & Information Centre Ltd), see www.bl.uk/silkroad

ABOVE & BOTTOM LEFT
Mid-seventh-century glazed terracotta figurines of two female musicians, one in Kuchean dress playing the *pipa* (lute), the other in Chinese dress playing the *jiegu* (drum)

FAR RIGHT
Mid-seventh-century Chinese terracotta figurine of a female dancer or 'twirling girl'

BELOW
Painted clay Chinese tomb monster, designed to ward off evil spirits

Gallery Talks with Expert Guides

Tuesdays at 6.15pm; admission free.
No need to book, just meet in the Gallery

11 May **Sam van Schaik:**
The Tibetan Empire and Tibetan
Buddhism on the Silk Road

8 June **Susan Whitfield:**
Silk Road Women – Abandoned
Wives and Polo Players

22 June **Ursula Sims-Williams:**
The Kingdom of Khotan

31 August **Frances Wood:**
The Cave Temples at Dunhuang

Concert

Mahler's 'Das Lied' Revisited
Saturday 14 August, 6.00pm
Entrance Hall, The British Library

Robynne Redmon *mezzo-soprano*
Warren Mok *tenor*
Chamber Orchestra Anglia
Sharon Andrea Choa *conductor (inset right)*

In eighth-century Tang dynasty China, the poets Li Bai, Qian Qi, Meng Haoran and Wang Wei all bemoaned their failure to win fame and fortune in verse while drowning their sorrows in drink. Some 1,200 years later, while suffering family tragedy and ill health, Mahler came across these poems in German translation – a chance encounter of disparate lives and cultures united in sorrow that gave birth to his song-symphony *Das Lied von der Erde* (being performed in Prom 57). This new chamber ensemble version (arranged by Glen Cortese and Daniel Ng) resets the original Chinese texts to Mahler's music.
Tickets: £10 (concessions £7.50)

Lectures

Frantz Grenet: From Samarkand to Xi'an – the Sogdian Self-Image

Monday 10 May, 6.30pm
Conference Centre
Supported by the Committee
for Central and Inner Asia

Samarkand was the capital of Sogdiana, a kingdom of the ancient Silk Road. Sogdiana no longer exists but its history and culture remain as intriguing as ever. In this illustrated talk, Professor Grenet, of the École Pratique des Hautes Études in Paris, discusses how the Sogdians portrayed themselves in art.
Admission free, by ticket only

Frances Wood: Sir Aurel Stein and the Silk Road

Monday 28 June, 6.30pm
Conference Centre

In the last years of the 19th century, the Silk Road attracted a new type of traveller, the explorer-archaeologist. One of the greatest was Aurel Stein who made a series of epic trips through Central Asia, map-making, note-taking and collecting in the long-abandoned oasis sites along the Silk Road. Dr Frances Wood is Head of Chinese, Manchu & Mongolian Collections at the British Library.
Tickets: £5 (concessions £3.50)

Displays *Admission free*

Silk Road Photographs
18 June – 12 September

Photographs (many never previously displayed), taken by archaeologists, explorers, artists, administrators and amateur travellers, that illustrate the varied landscapes, peoples and ways of life in Chinese Central Asia (now Xinjiang) from the late 19th century until today.

Silk Threads 1 August – 12 September
Supported by East

Taking their inspiration from items in the Silk Road exhibition, fashion students from London's Central St Martins College of Art and Design have created paper designs for women's wear and print.

BRITISH LIBRARY

The British Library,
96 Euston Rd,
London NW1
Tel. 020 7412 7332;
textphone
020 7387 0626

Public Opening Hours *Admission free*
Weekdays 9.30am–6.00pm
(8.00pm on Tuesdays)
Saturdays 9.30am–5.00pm
Sundays/Bank Holidays 11.00am–5.00pm

The British Library is the UK's national library and home to some of the world's most exciting and significant books, manuscripts, maps, music, recorded sound and philatelic items from all cultures and from all periods of civilisation.

The Reading Rooms are open to those needing to do research or unable to find the material they need elsewhere. Areas open to the general public include the exhibition galleries, bookshop, café and restaurant.

Tickets for the concert and lectures are bookable by phone on 020 7412 7222; by e-mail to boxoffice@bl.uk; or at the British Library Information Desk

143

Proms Composer Portraits

Lecture Theatre, Victoria & Albert Museum (Exhibition Road entrance)

Recorded for broadcast on BBC Radio 3 later the same day, immediately following the main evening Prom. Admission is free but availability is limited. Tickets can be collected from the Proms Information Desk at the V&A from an hour beforehand. Latecomers will not be admitted until a suitable break in the performance.

Proms Composer Portraits feature music for chamber ensemble by four distinguished composers, three of whom have newly commissioned works being performed at the Proms this year.

In these early-evening events, the composers, in conversation with BBC Radio 3's Andrew McGregor *(below left)*, will discuss their works being heard in the main-evening Prom, as well as presenting a different aspect of their creative activities through smaller-scale pieces which will be performed by young musicians from leading music colleges and conservatoires around the UK. The series opens with the Chinese-American composer, Zhou Long, and continues with three leading figures in British contemporary music today: John Casken, Sir Peter Maxwell Davies and Sir Harrison Birtwistle.

Zhou Long
Tuesday 20 July, 6.00pm
(before Prom 6)
Dhyana, for flute, clarinet, violin, cello and piano; *Su (Tracing Back)*, for flute and harp; *Five Maskers*, for brass quintet
Musicians from the Guildhall School of Music & Drama

John Casken
Thursday 22 July, 6.00pm
(before Prom 8)
Blue Medusa, for bassoon and piano; *The Haunting Bough*, for piano; *Nearly Distant*, for saxophone quartet
Adam Swayne (piano), Musicians from the Royal Northern College of Music

Sir Peter Maxwell Davies
Wednesday 4 August, 5.30pm (before Prom 27)
Quartet Movement; Little Quartet No. 1; Little Quartet No. 2; Dove, Star-Folded, for string trio; *Midhouse Air*, for violin and viola
Artea String Quartet (from the Royal Academy of Music)

Sir Harrison Birtwistle
Tuesday 17 August, 6.00pm
(before Prom 43)
Refrains and Choruses, for wind quintet; *Nocturnes from 'The Io Passion'*, for clarinet and string quartet; *Nine Settings of Lorine Niedecker*, for soprano and cello
Contemporary Consort of the Royal College of Music

Proms Question Time

Broken Sounds? Reinventing the symphony orchestra for the 21st century

Friday 13 August, c10.00pm–10.45pm
Royal Albert Hall, West Arena Foyer
Admission free to ticket-holders for Prom 38

The two works in Prom 38 – Olivier Messiaen's *Turangalîla Symphony* and *The Song and Dance of Tears* by Bright Sheng *(above)* – both present a radical approach to orchestral sound and practice. In this post-Prom event, Christopher Cook *(right)* chairs a debate about the role of the symphony orchestra in a changing world. How can it remain relevant in an ever more culturally diverse environment? How can the orchestra maintain its edge in a competitive technological age? Where do musicians, conductors, composers and audiences fit in? What is the impact of specialist period-instrument and new-music ensembles on the standard symphony orchestra? And to what extent should we be trying to preserve the historical traditions of the orchestra?

The panel – including Bright Sheng and David Robertson, conductor of the evening's concert – will answer questions put to it both by the audience in the Hall and by listeners at home, via text and e-mail.

For details, see www.bbc.co.uk/proms

Pre-Prom Talks & Events

RAH •
Royal Albert Hall
(Auditorium: Door 6)

RCM •
Royal College of Music

RCA •
Royal College of Art

*Admission is free to
ticket-holders for the
following Prom*

BELOW
Nijinsky's costume for *Le
Festin*, designed by Léon Bakst
and worn on the opening
night of the Ballets Russes'
first Paris season in 1909, is
one of over 500 costumes
from Diaghilev productions
held in the collections of the
V&A Theatre Museum

Sunday 18 July, 5.00pm **RAH**
Writer and broadcaster Piers Burton-Page on
Dvořák's rarely performed grand opera *Dimitrij*

Monday 19 July, 5.30pm **RCM**
'England at the Crossroads: 1934': Proms
Director Nicholas Kenyon and conductor
Richard Hickox discuss our season theme

Wednesday 21 July, 6.00pm **RCM**
An overview of the season's Czech/Bohemian
theme by writer and broadcaster Jan Smaczny

Friday 23 July, 6.00pm **RAH**
Composer-conductor George Benjamin discusses
his music and that of his teacher, Olivier Messiaen

Saturday 24 July, 6.00pm **RAH**
Sakari Oramo discusses Ives's Symphony No. 4
with CBSO Chief Executive, Stephen Maddock

Wednesday 28 July, 5.30pm **RCM**
Dennis Marks discusses Janáček's *Glagolitic Mass*
with Petr Fiala, director of the guest chorus
from the composer's home town of Brno

Sunday 1 August, 5.00pm **RCM**
Composer Colin Matthews discusses Britten's
War Requiem with Tommy Pearson

Monday 2 August, 6.00pm **RAH**
Chinese-American composer-conductor
Tan Dun introduces tonight's programme

Thursday 5 August, 6.00pm **RAH**
Swedish composer Anders Hillborg discusses his
new work *Exquisite Corpse* with Andrew Kurowski

Sunday 8 August, 5.00pm **RAH**
Writer and broadcaster Roderick Swanston
introduces Dvořák's oratorio *The Spectre's Bride*

Tuesday 10 August, 6.00pm **RAH**
A discussion about the music of Heinrich Biber

Wednesday 11 August, 6.00pm **RAH**
Piers Burton-Page introduces Mahler's
ground-breaking Symphony No. 7

Friday 13 August, 6.00pm **RAH**
Bright Sheng talks to Gillian Moore about his
concerto for the Silk Road Project

Sunday 15 August, 6.30pm **RCM**
Sir John Eliot Gardiner on Bach's B minor Mass

Monday 16 August, 6.00pm **RAH**
Russian music specialist David Nice discusses
the genesis of Rimsky-Korsakov's *Mlada*

Wednesday 18 August, 6.00pm **RCM**
Malcolm MacDonald introduces Hans Werner
Henze's Symphony No. 10

Thursday 19 August, 4.45pm **RCA**
OAE musicians and students from Camden
explore the fascinating themes of *Das Rheingold*

Thursday 19 August, 5.30pm **RAH**
John Deathridge introduces *Das Rheingold*, the
first opera in Wagner's epic *Ring* cycle

Friday 20 August, 5.30pm **RAH**
Hansel and Gretel: Mark Lowther on
Humperdinck's operatic version of a Grimm tale

Sunday 22 August, 5.00pm **RAH**
Composer-conductor John Adams introduces
his latest works to be heard at the Proms

Thursday 26 August, 6.00pm **RAH**
Nicholas Payne, director of Opera Europa,
introduces Glyndebourne's new double-bill

Saturday 28 August, 5.00pm **RAH**
Leading Berio specialist David Osmond-Smith
discusses the influences behind Berio's work

Tuesday 31 August, 6.00pm **RAH**
The conductor Robert King talks about his
passion for Monteverdi's *Vespers of 1610*

Wednesday 1 September, 6.00pm **RAH**
John Corigliano in conversation with John Allison

Thursday 2 September, 5.30pm **RAH**
Joby Talbot talks to Mark Russell

Monday 6 September, 5.45pm **RAH**
Audience Forum: your chance to put questions
to Proms Director Nicholas Kenyon and David
Elliott, Chief Executive of the Royal Albert Hall

Tuesday 7 September, 6.00pm **RAH**
Kaija Saariaho discusses her new work *Orion*
with critic and broadcaster Tom Service

Wednesday 8 September, 5.30pm **RCM**
Stephanie Hughes talks to members of the
Czech Philharmonic Orchestra

Thursday 9 September, 6.00pm **RAH**
William Christie discusses the music
of Marc-Antoine Charpentier with
Edward Blakeman

The return of 'Performing Art'

Performing Art – the series of popular
pre-concert talks run in partnership with the
V&A – is not only back in place before this
season's Monday-lunchtime Proms Chamber
Music concerts *(see pages 120–21)* but can
also now be heard exclusively online, with each
talk available to listen to via the BBC Proms
website from the morning after it takes place.

You can also take a look at the objects being
discussed and follow links to the relevant and
related collections on the V&A's website.
And, in the run-up to the season, there will
be competitions, with chances to win tickets
to both *Performing Art* talks and Proms
Chamber Music concerts. For details visit
www.bbc.co.uk/proms/performingart

Countdown to Prom 1

Broadcasting the Proms is a performance in itself, requiring months of planning and a cast of hundreds. Seven key players in the process here reveal the thoughts that will be going through their heads at 7.29pm on the First Night

Oliver Macfarlane 19:29:01
Editor, TV Classical Music

'One minute to the Albert Hall' calls the voice over the loudspeaker. In the TV scanner outside the Hall we are listening to the Network Director at Television Centre guiding us like an air traffic controller onto the runway for a smooth take-off onto the airways of BBC2. It's the first of many: this year we're televising 30 Proms on BBC1, BBC2 and BBC4 – most of them live. But on the First Night, as with several other Proms this season, the presentation is heard on Radio 3 as well as BBC2 so everything has to work in sound as well as pictures.

Working closely with presenter Stephanie Hughes, my Radio 3 colleagues and the Proms team, the script has been written and re-written and video-taped inserts edited and scrutinised to make the broadcast as engaging as possible for both viewers and listeners and to help the concert run as smoothly as possible for the audience in the Hall.

Last-minute questions run through my mind: are the cues to Stephanie and Backstage in the right place for the opening sequence? A quick check of my marked-up script suggests they are. Our interview guests are all here and in the right place – but will the conductor and soloist make it up to the presenter's box in time for a live interview during the interval? A glance at the timings on the running-order again indicates it will be tight but manageable. Am I still in communication with everyone I need to talk to beyond the TV scanner?

'30 seconds to the Albert Hall.' A trailer is running on our BBC2 preview monitor. I press the button marked 'R3' and give Edward a 30-second standby. He acknowledges. I press the button marked 'Pres' and I see Stephanie smile and nod on her preview monitor. And finally I press the 'Backstage' button to the TV floor manager to check that the orchestra is ready for its tuning cue and that conductor Leonard Slatkin is standing by. Reassuringly, all is well.

'10 seconds.' Our PA is counting down to zero in sync with the Network Director at TV Centre. The opening titles are rolling and suddenly our pictures are on air on BBC2. As the titles end, it's cue Stephanie – 'Welcome to the Royal Albert Hall …' – and the great musical jumbo is airborne once again.

Edward Blakeman 19:29:01
Editor, Live Music, BBC Radio 3

One minute to go. The mobile phone announcement has just been played (newly-recorded using my phone, so I really must remember to turn it off!) and we are waiting to go 'on air' – for the parachute to open! No other moment feels quite like this one, just as nothing else ever feels quite like the Proms.

This is also the beginning of a new pattern of days, of life lived in transit between Broadcasting House and the Hall, for the next eight weeks. My job is to pull the whole broadcasting operation together, so it's a mixture of planning and doing – and, most importantly, being here.

It all started back at the end of last season: taking stock, learning from what did or didn't go well, beginning to discuss and plan. But things got going in earnest with the first technical meeting back in February. By then the concert schedule is pretty well finalised, the Proms Guide about to go to press, and we can see the shape of the whole season. Which are the days with two or even three concerts, the tricky events, the impossible (almost) turn-arounds? Which producers and presenters will best suit which concerts? And what about the intervals and interviews and the whole raft of related programming that Radio 3 puts around the Proms? The list goes on. Five months – and a lot of meetings, e-mails and phone calls – later, this is the moment of truth. Or rather, the first of a whole series of moments.

I sometimes think the Proms are like a summer repertory season, except that the 'play' changes every night! The drama of the next eight weeks will be played out for radio in two small, darkened spaces: Loggia Box 2 inside the Hall, and the digital sound vehicle (DSV) outside Door 11. Building that studio within and without the Hall has been the great challenge of 'Rig Week' over the last few days. Countless flight cases have disgorged all sorts of equipment and hundreds of metres of cabling. Gradually all the connections have been made, the communications established – talkback is the lifeline of live radio! – the familiar festoon of microphones slung high above the stage. It's great to be back, it always is. And when those first notes sound, we really will be back. So it's '10 seconds … and standby … and here we go!'

19:29:59

Stephanie Hughes
19:29:01
Presenter, Radio and TV

'That's a minute to "on air", Stephanie.' The familiar sound of my television director in my earpiece. I open my mouth for a last daub of lip gloss from the make-up artist, and turn round to look across the Hall. I grin at the Prommers below and give a thumbs-up to the Radio 3 crew in the Loggia box. It's a joint TV and radio broadcast, and everyone wants the First Night to be a cracking start to the season. My eyes turn to the orchestra. They're all in position. I see the floor manager lingering by the Bull Run ready to cue the leader and the conductor.

'That's 30.' I swing round to my own broadcasting area in the Grand Tier. Camera and sound men wait. I check the autocue – the opening words are there. I know them by heart, but it's comforting to see them. I clutch the microphone and feel the heat from the television lights above. I take a final swig of water and flick through the stack of paper at my feet – a hard copy of the script, biographies of the soloists, extra material on the pieces, on the Hall, on the event, observations on the day so far – just in case anything happens and I need to fill.

The 2 of the BBC2 logo is dancing around on the monitor and continuity is handing over to the Royal Albert Hall. The opening titles begin, and my floor manager crouches below the camera to count me out of the VT. I take a huge breath and smile. 'That's 10 seconds, Stephanie … and 5, 4, 3, 2 …' Boy, do I have one of the best jobs in the world!

Helen Mansfield
19:29:01
Producer, TV Classical Music

After months of preparation, here I am, sitting with the production team in the scanner outside the Hall and checking the opening shots for all the nine cameras. By this stage, vision mixer Priscilla Hoadley will have rehearsed every cut and timed it to precision; production assistant Michael Ledger will have prepared every on-screen camera move with a bar-by-bar count, starting at the beginning of the musical phrase and settling by the end; and of course, like any director, I can rely on the immense skill of the camera crew and their outside broadcast colleagues. Yet, I reflect, although there are over 60 TV personnel here now – plus our radio colleagues – back in the spring it was just me, my score and my CD player.

The director's work starts with listening to the music again and again, going through the score with a fine toothcomb, planning the most appropriate camera shots to cover every bar of music. The script is written directly on to the orchestral score and each of the cameras is given a set of cards, with every shot numbered and described. You have to anticipate possible pitfalls. Before the first rehearsal my score was covered in bright yellow 'post-its' - 'BEWARE – HORNS – WHO PLAYS? – PRINCIPAL OR BUMPER?' 'CYMBALS – WHICH SET?' 'SOLOIST'S MICROPHONE POSITION – CHECK' 'WAIT for Leonard's downbeat' 'XYLOPHONE – PLAYER WITH GLASSES?'

Now I can only hope that the shots I planned will complement the conductor's ambition for the music – and that the script will as far as possible portray the great sense of event in the Hall. Last-minute changes, though, are all part of the job and, during any live transmission, I always keep a camera on the conductor to cut to if anything doesn't go to plan. But for now, as I wish Stephanie Hughes and the team good luck, and Camera 3 pans elegantly across the Hall, I know that my script is in the best possible hands.

Bruce Miller
19:29:01
Camera supervisor, TV OBs

This afternoon's rehearsal with the orchestra went well – great music and the director had done an excellent camera script. The few shots that didn't work properly, we sorted out in the notes session afterwards. The director has also just given me some late camera shot changes over the talkback: I'm now doing the oboe solo and another camera will take the shot of the flute. I wonder now which horn will play in the second movement. We never quite established that! I'll maybe make the framing of the picture a little wider, just in case.

The Prommers have now finished filing into the Arena. I recognise a few faces from previous seasons spent standing behind my camera in the Grand Tier Box. I take a final look through my camera shot cards. Then it's on with the glasses, and here's to a smooth show!

ABOVE
Stephanie Hughes: your host for the First Night on both BBC2 and Radio 3

Steve Dunn `19:29:01`
Engineering Manager, TV OBs

Sitting in the OB truck, I glance briefly around the production area. I can see the concentration on the faces of my colleagues illumined by the glow from the stack of TV monitors. I catch the eye of the director and the vision-mixer and give them a quick smile and a 'thumbs-up'. To my left in the truck is the vision control and engineering area and through the glass panel I can see the vision supervisor and his engineers looking after the picture quality, for people viewing at home. At the other end of the truck is the Sound area, where the sound mix for the presenter and the guests is prepared; the music mix is done in a separate truck parked alongside.

I call a quick 'Have a good one' on the engineering intercom and get a nod back from the guys I can see. I briefly muse at how lucky I am to be working with such skilled professionals. As the countdown to 'on air' goes on in the background, I think back over all the work that's been done since the first planning meeting in May – booking camera, sound and engineering crews, rigging cables, sorting out vehicles and access, liaising with the Hall and the Proms management, so we cause one another the minimum amount of fuss.

I quickly snap out of my reverie as the countdown reaches '10 seconds'. Everything is working fine and we go on air, with the first broadcast of another Proms season. A great team effort, and a great team to be part of.

Neil Pemberton `19:29:01`
Senior Studio Manager, Radio & Music

As the Radio 3 technical team relax in the DSV outside the Albert Hall, calm and confident that we have completed all essential pre-transmission tests, I can't help recalling past broadcasts that have not gone exactly according to plan.

Who doesn't remember John Holmstrom's heroics at the microphone on The Night The Piano Lift Got Stuck? (I was standing on it at the time, but vigorously deny any causal link.) It's less well-known, though, that the evening was only saved by teams of Arena Prommers hand-cranking the recalcitrant under-stage machinery in perspiring relays.

Radio gremlins have chalked up an impressive tally of hits against the Proms. Presenter Penny Gore famously broadcast almost an entire first half using her headset mike when the electrical supply to the mixing-desk suddenly ceased. Seated at that same mixing-desk for the premiere of Judith Weir's *Moon and Star*, I flinched as the lights on the console did a Mexican Wave. It soon became clear that the ship had been taken over by paranormal forces that considered my presence superfluous.

Formative experiences such as these mould the broadcast engineer into an Eeyore-ish figure, always setting out reserve microphones for the musical glitterati, and never, ever forgetting to do likewise for the presenter who, if the diva croaks mid-phrase or the flamboyant fiddler's E string twangs into oblivion, must steer us from calamity to serenity.

Get MORE from BBC Proms radio and TV broadcasts …

MORE information about the music, with programme notes now available to read on radio, TV and online:
- On radio – for listeners on DAB Digital Radio and Freeview
- On TV – for digital viewers at the press of their red button
- Online – from the website at www.bbc.co.uk/proms

MORE choice of Last Night concerts for Digital TV viewers: Press your red button to choose between
- The Last Night of the Proms in the Royal Albert Hall
- BBC Proms in the Park in Hyde Park, London
- BBC Proms in the Park around the UK – this year in Belfast, Glasgow and Swansea *(for digital satellite and cable viewers only)*

MORE interactivity:
- Put your questions to Proms artists
- Tell us what you think of Proms performances
- Win Proms tickets

Full details from the Proms website – www.bbc.co.uk/proms

The first Proms concert took place on 10 August 1895 and was the brainchild of the impresario Robert Newman, manager of the newly built Queen's Hall in London.

Manuel de Falla *La Vida Breve* **BBC**

 **90-93 FM**

Proms on BBC Radio 3

Every Prom is broadcast live on BBC Radio 3 and many can be heard again on weekday afternoons at 2.00pm.

Proms Chamber Music concerts are all broadcast live and repeated the following Saturday at 12.00 noon.

Proms Composer Portraits (*see page 144*) are broadcast later the same day.

Twenty Minutes programmes, broadcast in the intervals of evening Proms, include features and talks around the year's Proms themes and anniversaries.

In Tune (weekdays, 5.00–7.30pm) features Proms-related interviews, performances, news and the winning works in the BBC Proms/Guardian Young Composers Competition.

Morning on 3 (weekdays, 7.00–10.00am; weekends, 7.00–9.00am) will carry updates on the season.

Listen out too for the following special Proms-related programming:

Proms Preview Evening
(Monday 12 July, 7.30–10.30pm)
Musical highlights and the inside story on the coming season.

Summer Selection
(Saturdays, 9.00am–12.00 noon)
Guest presenters – including Simon Russell Beale, Richard Eyre, Jackie Kay and Robert Winston – make their pick of forthcoming Proms alongside other choices.

Performing Janáček
(Saturdays, 2.00–3.00pm)
Janáček's dramatic works are in the repertory of opera houses around the world, thanks to their vividly drawn characters, colourful and idiosyncratic scoring and creative challenges – for example, a singing frog jumping onto a forester's nose! In this series of eight programmes, Ivan Hewett talks to singers, conductors and producers about the unique demands and rewards of performing Janáček.

Proms Sunday Features

Sunday 25 July, 9.35pm
My Country
Art and politics in the melting-pot of the 19th-century Czech national revival and their continuing resonances today.

Sunday 1 August, 8.15pm
East Meets West Meets East
The many ways in which artists from Eastern traditions are refashioning and reinventing Western cultural classics.

Sunday 15 August, 9.50pm
A Renaissance Man?
Messiaen's work in the light of his multi-faceted character as Catholic, composer, organist, ornithologist and teacher.

Times subject to change

All broadcast details were correct at the time of going to press. For current schedules, consult *Radio Times* or other listings publications, or visit the Proms website – www.bbc.co.uk/proms

Proms on BBC World Service

The BBC World Service broadcasts regular highlights from the season. Details on www.bbc.co.uk/worldservice

BBC Proms Online

www.bbc.co.uk/proms

The BBC Proms website is the place to come for all the news and information you need on the season, including full sets of programme notes for all 74 RAH concerts and handy 'quick guides' and 'behind the scenes' features. You can book tickets online, post your views and questions on our popular message board, and even compete for tickets by submitting your own reviews. You can listen to every Prom online via the Radio 3 live stream and many Proms and Proms Chamber Music concerts will also be available for 'on demand' listening for up to seven days after broadcast. You can also help choose the programme for 'The Nation's Favourite Prom' by voting online (see *listing for Prom 2, page 99*).

Proms on BBC Television

BBC1
Proms 2, 21 and 42 will be recorded for later showing; Prom 74 (Part 2) will be shown live.

BBC2
Proms 1, 20, 31, 47, 57, 66 and 74 (Part 1) will be shown live.

BBC4
Proms 4, 6–9, 11, 13–16, 18–19, 21, 67–70 and 72–73 will be shown live. Prom 17 will be recorded for later showing.

BBC Proms 2004 Guide

Published by BBC Proms Publications.
Editorial Office: Room 4084, Broadcasting House, Portland Place, London W1A 1AA

Distributed by BBC Worldwide, 80 Wood Lane, London W12 0TT

Editor Mark Pappenheim
Publications Manager Sarah Breeden
Editorial Manager David Threasher
Publications Officer Suzanne Esdell
Publications Assistant Hannah Rowley

Design Premm Design Ltd, London
Cover photograph (RAH) Simon Keats
Advertising Cabbell Publishing Ltd, London
Printed by Taylor Bloxham Ltd, Leicester

© BBC 2004
ISBN 0-563-52166-X

BBC Proms 2004

Director Nicholas Kenyon CBE, Controller, BBC Proms, Live Events and TV Classical Music
Personal Assistant Yvette Pusey

Artistic Administrator Rosemary Gent
Concerts Administrator Helen Burridge
Acting Concerts Administrator Phil Boughton
Concerts Assistants Lucy Crisfield, Emma Syrus

Marketing Manager Kate Finch
Publicist Victoria Bevan
Marketing and Audience Development Officer Doug Buist
Marketing & Publicity Assistant Jacqui Garbett

Finance Manager David Stott
Finance Assistant Tricia Twigg

Editor, Live Music, BBC Radio 3 Edward Blakeman
Editor, TV Classical Music Oliver Macfarlane

THE PROMS COLLECTION

THE PERFECT GIFT

AVAILABLE FROM THE ROYAL ALBERT HALL

BBC
PROMS

Académies Musicales de Saintes, France
14-25 july 2004

information and tickets on line, www.festival-saintes.org

BACH, BEETHOVEN
BRUCKNER, COUPERIN
DE KERLE, DEBUSSY
DUFAY, GESUALDO
GLASS, HAYDN
JOSQUIN DES PRES
KURTAG, LASSUS
LIGETI, MAHLER
MESSIAEN, MOZART
RACHMANINOV
RAVEL, SCHOECK
SCHUBERT, SCRIABIN
SVIRIDOV, SWEELINCK
WILLAERTS

STEPHAN MACIEJEWSKI
artistic director

ACCENTUS CHAMBER CHOIR
THOMAS BAUER
COLLEGIUM VOCALE GENT
DAEDALUS ENSEMBLE
FREIBURGER BAROCK ORCHESTER
JEAN-FRANÇOIS HEISSER
JOS VAN IMMERSEEL
MAREK JANOWSKI
JEUNE ORCHESTRE ATLANTIQUE
MARIE JOSEPHE JUDE
PHILIPPE HERREWEGHE
HUELGAS ENSEMBLE
ORCHESTRE DES CHAMPS-ELYSÉES
ORCHESTRE POITOU-CHARENTES
QUATUOR MINGUET
JEAN GUILHEN QUEYRAS
DANIEL REUSS
CAROLYN SAMPSON
ANDREAS STAIER
ALEXANDRE THARAUD

"Every music festival can lay claim to its own particular magic. But it's doubtful you'll find anywhere quite like the Académies Musicales in Saintes. It's a place where musicians, critics and audience are permanently engaged in spirited conversation, from dissections of last night's concert to anticipations of tomorrow's revelations.

One moment you can be sitting in the audience behind a pioneer of early music ; the next you're sharing a bottle or two of Bordeaux with musicians from the resident band.

And though the late-night revelry might indicate otherwise, there can be no doubting that this gathering is dedicated to one thing : music performance of the very highest standard."

Andrew Clarke, The Independent

Index of Artists

Bold italic figures refer to Prom numbers
(PCM indicates Proms Chamber Music concerts: see pages 120–21).
* First appearance at a BBC Henry Wood Promenade Concert

Index of Works

Bold italic figures refer to Prom numbers (PCM indicates Proms Chamber Music concerts: see pages 120–21).
* First performance at a BBC Henry Wood Promenade Concert

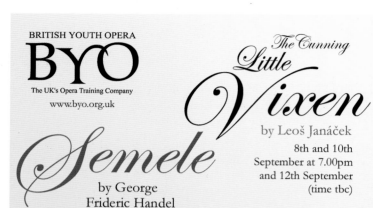

BRITISH YOUTH OPERA

BYO

The UK's Opera Training Company

www.byo.org.uk

The Cunning
Little
Vixen

by Leoš Janáček

8th and 10th
September at 7.00pm
and 12th September
(time tbc)

Semele

by George
Frideric Handel

7th, 9th and 11th September at 7.00pm

Queen Elizabeth Hall

on the South Bank

Box Office: 0870 380 0400 Tickets: £8 - £22

(Booking opens 31st May)

THE BACH CHOIR

Concert Season 2004/05

Tuesday 19 October 2004
Royal Festival Hall
Beethoven *Missa Solemnis*

Friday 19 November 2004
St George's Chapel, Windsor
Works by Naji Hakim, Liszt,
Parry, Tavener, Tchaikovsky,
Tippett, Randall Thompson
& Vaughan Williams

Sunday 12 December 2004
Royal Albert Hall
The Bach Choir Family Carols

Wednesday 2 February 2005
Royal Festival Hall
JS Bach *B Minor Mass*

Sundays 13 & 20 March 2005
Royal Festival Hall
JS Bach *St Matthew Passion*

Wednesday 20 April 2005
Royal Festival Hall
Walton *Belshazzar's Feast*
Richard Blackford
Voices of Exile

Wednesday 11 May 2005
Royal Festival Hall
Works by **Tippett, Britten**
& Burrell

Wednesday 25 May 2005
St George's Chapel, Windsor
Haydn *Nelson Mass*
Mozart *Solemn Vespers*

All concerts
conducted
by David Hill

For more details, please
phone 020 8742 3661
or visit our website:
www.thebachchoir.org.uk

Concert details may be
subject to change

Discover the Rhythm of Life

See Britain's most impressive display of musical instruments brought to life in a breathtaking new gallery

'A world class gallery celebrating music'

Jools Holland,
Horniman Museum
Patron

HORNIMAN MUSEUM

100 London Road • Forest Hill • SE23
FREE admission • Tel 020 8699 1872

Free
parking in
surrounding streets
Train Forest Hill